HYPNOTIC DETOX

Recipes for Well-Being

For cheryl,
Sending you happy hypnotic hugs!

4/15

LOIS R. BROWN

Hypnotic Detox: Recipes for Well-Being

Copyright © 2015 by Lois R. Brown

To contact the publisher, visit
www.ThePrincetonCenterForHealth.com

To contact the author, visit
www.HypnoticDetox.com

ISBN: 978-0-9961345-0-7

Printed in the United States of America

TABLE OF **CONTENTS**

DEDICATION

Perhaps the one person who helped me pull this all together and who taught me the most about the nature of health and change is Joshua Rosenthal, the founder of the Institute for Integrative Nutrition based in New York. Joshua continues to inspire me and thousands of others. He helped make this book possible with his out-of-the-box thinking, and by helping me realize that we *all* already have the courage, the brains and the heart to do whatever we choose. He is a true wizard.

I also dedicate this book to my father, Irwin Rosenberg, for unknowingly introducing me to hypnosis and also allowing me to take the TV apart while I was still a kid in kindergarten. To my mother, Sylvia Rosenberg, for teaching me that I could do anything I truly desired. If she saw her children climbing the cherry tree in our backyard, unlike most mothers who might say, "Come down before you hurt yourselves," Sylvia would look up and call out to us, "Keep going and you will reach the stars in the sky."

While external knowledge is certainly important, the internal love and unyielding support of my husband, Christopher Brown and our amazing son, David, are as important to me as the air I breathe. My husband is my writing-muse, and I am forever grateful for all of those days when I did not feel like writing and Chris lovingly and *firmly* kept me on track. David is my amuse-muse. His laser-precise suggestions and laughter were with me with each and every word I wrote.

ACKNOWLEDGEMENTS

My philosophy in life is that if you truly want something, you go after it with unabashed passion and massive actions. During my quest to learn about hypnosis, I embraced every opportunity to study directly with many of the leaders in the field. I received a certification as a Master NLP Practitioner under its cofounder, Dr. Richard Bandler, and a certificate in Advanced Parts Therapy and Medical Hypnosis under my dear friend and mentor, Dr. Jamie Feldman. I learned basic hypnosis techniques in Chicago with Barbara Stepp. whom I met while studying Neuro Associative Conditioning (NAC) with its creator and major motivational speaker, Tony Robbins. I even became a graduate of his Trainers Academy in California.

My thirst for knowledge continues to lead me to amazing teachers such as Gerald Kein, Tom Nicoli, and Don Mottin. I have been incredibly lucky to have very talented family, who I have learned so much from over the years. Thank you, Dr. Ronald Rosenberg and my amazing sister-in-law, Dr. Sarah Rosenberg, and thank you, Marshal Rosenberg for bringing the joy of music into my life. My dear cousin, Moshe Devere, thank you for your courage and honesty.

Much appreciation to my longtime friend and confidante, Rosalyn Fox, as well as my newest friends, Daisy and Wil Elmes, Deborah and Mike Raab, and my writing accountability buddy, Justine Bauer. Your friendships are the true elixir of life.

My dear friend, Nurse Patricia Crilly, has been a major inspiration to me and taught me the mind-blowing changes that Emotional Freedom Technique (EFT) aka Tapping can bring about. Pat has generously allowed me to utilize parts of her book, *Tap It and Zap It* to help me help you learn this quick and effective tool.

Cheers to all of the amazing teachers and friends I learned from at the Institute for Integrative Nutrition in New York City. What a joy you all are and how wonderful to be walking this crazy yellow brick road together!

I am totally indebted to four wonderful health leaders and chefs, Christina Pirello, Christine Waltermyer, Rochelle Blank-Zimmer and Andrea Beaman for instilling in me a needed sense of confidence and fun when it comes to health and the power of cooking. Skol!!

This book would not even be possible if it were not for the amazing clients I have worked with over the past twenty years. I enjoy working with each of you (you know who you are) and appreciate all that we have been able to accomplish together and learn from each other. I so look forward to those clients yet to come..

- A special acknowledgement to the journey of Dorothy and *The Wizard of Oz* and the quotes used here in this book.

FORWARD

Many of us are aware of the power of our thoughts; the power of the mind. We hear clichés all the time: mind over matter, etc.

But how many of us have discovered ways to unlock the potential of this powerful tool-our mind-to create health and wellness?

I met Lois several years ago when she was an audience member at the taping of one of my television shows. I was warming up the audience, waxing rhapsodic about the joys of cooking. Taking questions from the audience, I fielded a lot of technique and cooking questions.

Lois' hand went up and she asked what the solution was if one had no time to cook. Feeling my oats that day, I gave her what my staff calls my 'tough love' answer and advised Lois to re-prioritize her life and cook if her health was of value to her.

I never gave the incident a second thought.

A few weeks later, I was teaching a 3-day hands-on cooking weekend and in walked Lois Brown. Seeing my obvious surprise, she said, "You told me to re-prioritize my life so here I am."

Lois has become a dear friend, an amazing cook and an expert in natural living and healing, delving deeply into any subject she studies until she masters it. When she decided to specialize in hypnosis, I was not surprised. Her warm and caring manner; her genuine empathy and care for humanity's well-being makes her the perfect person to guide you on your path to health.

The techniques presented in this book are sound and easy to approach. Lois has completely removed any anxiety factor you might have with hypnosis by making you an active participant in the process. With the workbook-style pages peppered throughout, you remain fully in charge of what you want to achieve with hypnosis and wellness with Lois as your wise guide.

Gentle, smart and fully present when you meet her, Lois brings those same qualities to this book to help guide humanity to well-being and balance.

Christina Pirello
Emmy Award winning host of 'Christina Cooks' on national
public television
Bestselling author
March, 2015

INTRODUCTION

MY STORY

" Toto, I've a feeling we're not in Kansas anymore."

My story has to begin with your story. Why are you here? What made you pick up and open this book? How do you intend to use the information and tools here? Are you curious about discovering a number of fun and easy techniques that may forever change your life or the lives of your clients, friends, coworkers, loved ones? What is your motivating force? What "drives" you? What do you want to change? Why are you willing to leave where you are now and go through the hypnotic tornado with me?

One constant that I have found in my travels and studies around the world is that *everyone* has *something* they want to change. Change is the force that keeps us alive and thriving. Change can also be toxic to our lives when it takes the form of disease, loss, profound sadness or stagnation. Whatever the result, change is *inevitable*. Whether we like it or not, we will change; we are changing right now with every breath we take in and release. What do you want to *reach for* and change? How willing are you to *shake things up* just a bit?

In our modern age, change appears to be happening faster and faster each year. New inventions and new means of connecting to information are creating changes at a dizzying pace. Just think about how often new versions of your computer and related programs come out, or a new version of your smart phone. It may well be that within 50 years, change will become *constant*. While much of the changes that happen in our lives may be out of our control, there is a surprising amount that we *can* control. My outcome in writing this book is for you to read, write, experiment, and above all have fun as you experience a new sense of empowerment. I want you, the reader, to learn how to recognize toxic elements in your life and take back ownership and control of your body. Understand that there are so many wonderful ways that you can grab a hold of that rudder of your own unique ship and steer the course of your life. First you need to know where it is you want your ship to take you to. What are the destinations you desire?

Perhaps you want to drop weight, sleep better, eliminate your fears, be more successful at your job, change your relationships, do better on tests and at school, be more physically active, rid yourself of chronic physical discomforts—we all have *something* we want to and *can* change. The key is knowing *what* it is in life that you *really* want. With this book I will share with you many easy and wonderful ways that hypnosis can help you figure out where you want to go and how to get there. I will be there with you as together we navigate to make the changes that your heart truly desires.

My first encounter with hypnosis came when I was a small child. I secretly watched as my father used self-hypnosis to help relieve severe headaches. At the time, in the late 1950s and early 1960s, hypnosis was enjoying a new rebirth with the works of such noted teachers as Dr. Milton Erickson and Dave Elman. It was spellbinding to observe as my father look into the mirror into his own eyes while whispering some magical words I could not quite hear. I had just seen the movie, The Wizard of Oz, and my father reminded me of that great wizard. How lucky that I could appreciate this at such a young age!

My father, Irwin Rosenberg, was a tall man of little words with wavy brown hair. He always wore wire rimmed glasses and he was introspective and very smart. He was a naval architect and an engineer by trade. During World War II he was stationed in New Mexico, where he worked on the Manhattan Project: the secret program that developed the atomic bomb. Post World War II, he started one of the first companies to develop and install commercial heating/air conditioning units in our mutually beloved birthplace of Pittsburgh, PA. He continued to work with the government, designing and installing radar installation. His children inherited his love for science. I have two amazing brothers. Ronald is a well-respected medical doctor and computer guru.. Marshal received his degree in physics, and he runs his own computer consulting business in New York City.

When I was in kindergarten, my father taught me how to take apart our 1950s TV and replace the tubes that occasionally burned out. He also got me started on the road to hypnosis.

At the time I thought hypnosis was a very private and secret matter. I could tell that this was clearly something that was unique and held great powers. I continued to think about hypnosis from those moments on. One thing I knew for sure, I had taken a peek *behind* the curtain, and I began to take the first steps that would bring me through the hypnotic tornado into a new and magical world.

From my mother, Sylvia, I gained both a deep love of the arts and the belief that I could do anything in life I wanted to do. As introspective as my father was, my mother was equally extrospective. She was also very practical and had a good mind for business as well as a fine operatic voice. She adored all people in any social situation. Her warm brown eyes, soft smile and infectious laugh made her an immediate people-magnet whenever she entered into a room. Needless to say, I gained much from both of them, with the exception of *not* having a very good singing voice.

Life happens and I received an undergraduate and master's degree in English Education at New York University. I met and married my soul mate and husband-muse, Chris. I joined the forces of corporate America and did quite well financially. I traveled the world as part of my job, something I really loved to do. I had an amazing apartment in New York City on the twenty-eighth floor that had a spectacular view of Manhattan. As wonderful as this life was, something was starting to stir inside me. The fascination with the power of the mind along with an intense interest in health and helping others was starting to bloom. What followed were years and years of study in hypnosis and nutrition counseling.

Armed with a thirst for this knowledge, I devoured many of the books and tapes that were available at the time. In my early 20s I discovered the genius of Dr. Milton Erickson, who is said to be the father of modern hypnosis. I quickly went on to read with delight all of the very unique and humorous works by his protégées, Dr. Richard Bandler and Dr. John Grinder, the creators of Neuro-Linguistic Programming (NLP) ** NLP is an approach to communication, personal development, and psychotherapy. It uses specific linguistic patterns of language that allows quick access to the subconscious mind to receive and act upon suggestions to positively change behaviors and thoughts. For a specific definition of NLP by its founders, Dr. Bandler and Dr. Grinder, please see Chapter 8.

My own firsthand experience with the power of hypnosis came when I was pregnant with our son, David. I explored the few hypnosis resources that could be found at the time. Everything appeared to somewhat focus only on minimizing the *discomfort* of labor. For an expectant mom the thought of going through a prolonged delivery filled with even mild *discomfort* was not a very comforting thought. I began to wonder if any of the authors of these hypnosis books and tapes, (all men at the time), had ever actually experienced seeing a woman giving birth after fifteen or twenty hours or more? For this reason I made my own self-hypnosis tapes and added the key suggestions that I wanted a *quick* and *healthy* delivery along with minimal discomfort.

The results were astounding. The day David was born I went to work as usual and started to have a bit of cramping mid-day. I then drove to the market to shop for food, and then drove home. Around 6:00 p.m. I asked my husband to drive me to the hospital. Two-and-a-half hours after I walked into the Princeton Medical Center, our son was born. I needed no medications and had no complications. What's more, I recovered very quickly and never experienced any negative side-affects from labor. I had no post-partum sadness. It was clear that my own personal experience with hypnosis in a major situation worked.

I was hooked! I wanted to put hypnosis into action with almost everything, and I focused on a new quest: to share this with others. Not only did I want to help people make the changes they wanted, I wanted to teach them how do this for themselves. My means of study quickly shifted gears and I was extremely fortunate to meet, study with, and become certified by Dr. Bandler, Dr. Jaime Feldman, Barbara Stepp, and many other pioneers in the fields of hypnosis. Parts Therapy and N.L.P..

I chose a holistic approach to health, coaching and change and soon learned the importance of food to our overall well-being. To round off my cooking and wellness knowledge I connected with Christina Pirello, Christine Waltermyer, Rochelle Blank-Zimmer and Andrea Beaman – four amazing teachers and chefs. Each of these powerful women share the ability to teach and empower their students. This inspired me to became a certified health counselor through the Institute for Integrative Nutrition in New York City. Knowledge is a lifelong journey and I continue to learn how to support and serve others each and every day.

I tell you all of this not to *impress* you, but rather, as Tony Robbins would say, to *impress upon* you how this book and I can share with you the fun and magic of hypnosis to make changes that will last you a lifetime.

Now just take a moment. Step back and *breathe*, and just imagine what you will do as you unleash the power of your own mind. What can you do, have, or change as you too learn to create your own self-hypnosis?

INTRODUCTION

INSTRUCTIONS

How to Use This Book to Get Results

This book is constructed with many options to use when reading to get various levels of results. This depends upon what it is you are looking for. Is this a self-help book for yourself? Are you looking for new tools to help your clients get unstuck and move forward? How quickly do you want to see your outcomes? What level of change are you looking for?

Here are a few possibilities:
1. You can skim through this book and look at those areas that pique your interest.
2. You can read the Take-Aways section at the end of each chapter to get a general overview.
3. You can experiment with the Recipes at the end of each chapter to have a bit of fun and see how this works.
4. You can read a few pages at a time.
5. You can *consume* this book in record-breaking speed to take *everything* in.
6. You can read each chapter and skip the questions listed in each section and think, "Hey I came here to read, not write."

All of these strategies will still get you results of varying levels. If you are looking to get the maximum results in the *quickest* and most *efficient* period of time here is what I suggest:

1. Read one chapter at a time. Each builds upon the next. They are relatively short so this is very easy to do.
2. If you are new to the subject matter, feel free to read the book through and then go back and read each chapter for more detail.
3. Take the extra five or six minutes to write down the answers to the questions in each chapter. You can certainly do this in your mind; but the process of *writing something down* by hand sends mega-messages to your subconscious for new awareness and to get things moving.
4. When writing the answers, let things flow. Trust the words that are coming through and avoid overthinking. When we overthink we are using our conscious mind. When we let things flow naturally we are tapping into the resources of both the conscious and subconscious mind. This creates a very formidable and effective synergy.
5. Try not to read this book too quickly. The subconscious needs time to assimilate and process new information. Reading too much too fast may result in overload.
6. The most important tips of all: When using this book: read, write, and experiment with a sense of curiosity. *Don't hold back and be sure to play full out.*

We all know how easy it is for children to learn new languages and assimilate new skills. Part of this comes from having the physiology and mental skill to do so with a young brain. However there is so much more to this. Children also learn easily because they are naturally curious and playful and they love having fun. These abilities are ageless. Tap into them and you will be amazed at quickly you learn.

That's it. There are no right or wrong ways to do this. *You* bought this book and *you* now own it. You choose what you want to do. It is nice to have choices, yes?

CHAPTER ONE
DETOX-SHMETOX
"Lions and Tigers and Bears, Oh My!"

HOW DID WE GET STUCK IN ALL THIS MUCK?

What is all this talk about "detox" and "detoxing"? It seems everyone we know is going through a detox process, thinking it is the fastest way to change his or her life quickly to get happy and healthy. Since when did we become so focused with the strategy of aligning ourselves with people who have serious substance abuse issues and need to go through a structured "*process* or period of time in which one *abstains* from or *rids* the body of *toxic* or *unhealthy* substances" (*Oxford University Press Dictionary*). What is it that we fear so much in our lives that leads us to this path? Do we fully understand the concept of what detox means? Does abstaining from a toxic substance(s) for a specified period of time really work, or is there far more or far less needed to get us the change and results we desire?

Okay, let me come clean here (forgive the pun) and share with you how I ended up writing a book with the word *detox* in it, and why this is a different type of *detox* than you may have experienced before. Several months back I was participating in a large conference in New York City with other health professionals when someone shared that she was writing a book that publishers were fighting over to buy. She actually had not one but two literary agents working on her behalf and advances were over $500,000. What was the nature of her book? You guessed it: *health* and *detox*! We are fascinated by the concept of detox. We see on bookshelves: "The 14 Day Detox," "The 10 Day Detox," "The 8 Day Detox," "The Three Day Detox," "The 1 Day Detox, "The 30 Second Detox," "The Super Detox," "The Super Duper Detox." We are a nation that yearns to take back ownership of our bodies. We want to get clean and clear, start anew and be in control. My concern is that we think there is a specific and quick formula—a *magic bullet*—that when used for a brief period of time will bring nirvana and solve all of our problems.

That afternoon, I left the conference curious and inspired. Does lasting change happen if/when we try to *consciously* commit to depriving ourselves for a specified number of days or weeks? Think back to a time in the past when you made various New Year's resolutions to stop smoking, drop weight, be more patient with others, do better at work, or go to the gym just by *consciously* saying you would do this. If you did make these changes, how long did this last for you? Yet this is what we do over and over again. We seem clear about our demons—what we do not want ("lions and tigers and bears, oh my") —and we use the same old strategies over and over again each year. For most of us, most of the time this takes us nowhere. We rarely follow through. Remember the quote from Einstein, "The definition of insanity is doing the same thing over and over again and yet expecting different results." I wondered if there was a way I could help people detox with lasting results that would change their lives *forever?*

That evening over dinner I shared with my husband my curiosity about adding still *another* detox book to the dozens already out there. Chris took this all in with his patient and quiet wisdom and silently nodded his head. The next day he excitedly said he had an epiphany that morning, "Why don't you write a book about *hypnosis* and detox?" He reminded me that my clients come to me to eliminate *toxic* reactions to people, emotions, fears, chronic discomfort, and disempowering life styles that are diminishing their ability to be happy and healthy. I teach them that instead of taking someone else's word about how to change, through hypnosis they can tap into the power of their own subconscious., The subconscious is perhaps a million times stronger and more effective than the conscious mind and through self-hypnosis my clients have reached their personal goals. *Hypnotic Detox – Recipes for Well-Being* was born thanks to Chris, my husband-muse.

The truth is you, the reader, already have the heart, the courage, and the brains to get yourself out of the toxic muck.

HOW DO OUR TOXIC REACTIONS TO THOUGHTS, PEOPLE, FOODS, AND LIFESTYLE CHOICES STAND IN THE WAY OF LIVING THE LIFE WE WANT?

In order to understand how *toxic* reactions impact us, we should first be clear on what the *toxins* are. Do we really know what the word *toxic* means?

The *Oxford University Press Dictionary* (http://www.oxfordlearnersdictionaries.com/definition/english/toxic) defines toxic as:

- "Containing poison; poisonous."

- "Having a very unpleasant personality, especially in the way they like to control and influence other people in a dishonest way"

Interesting, yes? Now take a few minutes and complete the following four simple questions that will help prepare you for amazing life-lasting changes that will blow your mind! Do this **NOW**, don't skip ahead. Feel free to write in this book, or find a special *detox* journal. Put on your favorite upbeat music to get things moving, and let your thoughts just *flow*. If you get stuck, stand up and move. Write down what comes naturally to mind. If you have more than one toxin in your life, answer the four questions for each. Now go, be creative and *write*.

1. Can you think of a time, past or present, when people you know, jobs that you have, foods you eat, feelings and fears you experience --any lifestyle habit or situation --made you feel like you were being poisoned, or controlled in a dishonest way?

_____

_____

_____

_____

2. How did/does this toxin limit your life? How did/does this stand in your way? What has this cost you? Seriously, what has this toxin cost you in terms of money, people in or gone from your life, your health and longevity? Your career? Your feelings about yourself? How has this impacted your loved ones around you?

_____

_____

_____

_____

_____

_____

_____

_____

3. What would your life be like now if this toxic situation were to go away and end forever?

_____

_____

_____

_____

4. **What have you tried to do so far to get rid of these toxins and toxic responses? What worked? What did not work? Why?**

_____

_____

_____

_____

_____

STOP—go back and really write this down—write it out on a plain piece of paper, napkin, or shopping list—whatever you have near you. The process of writing is an important one as it triggers new "aha" moments that are necessary to move forward. Your subconscious loves to read what you write and will quickly act upon things that are clearly stated. So, if you skipped over this section (and *I know* who you are), go back and complete this before moving on. Are you stuck? Often when we get stuck we forget to breathe—not a good thing. If you are stuck, clear your mind with the cleansing breathing recipe provided at the end of this chapter.

Are you beginning to see, hear, or feel the impact that toxins were having in your life and what they were costing not only you, but also those you love? How will you be different as you notice these toxins being removed? How will your life change forever?

Congratulations! You have taken perhaps one of the first most important steps in getting rid of toxins in your life. . . . You have opened up new awareness about what is standing in your way: how it has impacted on you and others, and what new pathways are possible.

I am just curious: After completing these questions, by *any* chance, have you noticed a slight *shift* in the intensity of your perceptions of the toxins that were impacting on you? If so, please make a note of this here.

How are you viewing those "lions and tigers and bears, oh my" **now**?

_____

_____

_____

_____

_____

DOES CLASSIC DETOX REALLY WORK?

Now that you have successfully written about your toxic situation(s) here, let's take a look at the classic way of detoxing that I will tell you right now, does *not* work long-term for most people. Remember that classic detox involves consciously abstaining from the toxin(s) for a specified period of time. This is indeed a necessary step for those who are battling drug or substance abuse, however, this book is not meant as a substitute for this situation. This book is useful to *augment* and complement these therapies.

For the *vast majority* of people who are battling less life-threatening demons than drug and substance abuse, we already know that conscious abstinence and deprivation for a specified period of time simply does not work long-term for them. Yes, we all know someone who did indeed stick to going to the gym, dropped weight, changed their career path, or stopped smoking, and it *stuck*. I do want to acknowledge those people who *can* immediately stop by making the choice to stop.

My husband is one of these people.

For twelve years Chris was a habitual smoker. He could not be on the phone, drive a car, drink a cup of coffee, attend a social situation, or wake up without a cigarette in his hand. He smoked up to two packs a day. At the age of twenty-eight he was on vacation in Spain and following a nasty toothache, he made an immediate decision to stop smoking completely. He literally threw away all of the American-made cigarettes he had brought with him and **stopped**. It is nearly forty years since then, and he has not had a single cigarette since!

So why is it that some people seem to easily stop just by almost willing it so? Upon closer look, I believe there is something else going on behind the scenes for these people who appear to be able to go "cold-turkey." In Chris's case, just before leaving for Spain he had read a very intense article in *Reader's Digest* about the impact of smoking. Furthermore, he had just acquired a new girlfriend, me, who had become a very firm nonsmoker. All of this, combined with the aggravated toothache, was compelling enough to his subconscious to want to stop *immediately*.

This is also the case for those who keep their New Year's resolutions long-term. They all have in common the ability to collect an arsenal of compelling reasons to change that have been understood, accepted by, and acted upon by their subconscious mind. Please understand this, long-term change *must* include the resources of our subconscious mind.

The fantastic news about this *is* that, once we engage our subconscious mind in a clear and direct way, massive change can come about in literally a nanosecond and last a lifetime. The natural and relatively easy process of hypnotic detox is the perfect way to get through to the subconscious. Hypnotic detox does *not* use the tactics of depravation, but rather acknowledgment and determining healthier and better alternatives. Whahoo! Isn't this amazing! Please be patient: we will get to the nitty-gritty hands-on knowledge about the subconscious and hypnotic detox soon.

The next part of Hypnotic Detox involves an understanding of the nature of toxins and stress. How is it possible that people respond differently to the same toxins and stressors? Is it possible to *immunize* ourselves to the effects of toxins and stress?

KEY TAKE AWAYS:

- Classic Detox = the process or period of time in which one abstains from or rids the body of toxic or unhealthy substances.

- Classic Detox strategies do not work long-term.

- Hypnotic Detox = the natural process of enlisting the power of the subconscious to bring about lasting change without the use of deprivation or willpower.

- The meaning of toxic = Containing poison; poisonous. Having a very unpleasant personality, especially in the way they like to control and influence other people in a dishonest way.

- Lasting change must fully engage your subconscious.

- Write it down! If you have not done it yet, go back and answer the four questions in this chapter. Your subconscious loves it when you write down your thoughts. Doing this will speed up the process of achieving your own hypnotic detox.

- If you get stuck . . . BREATHE

DETOX RECIPE #1
Getting Unstuck and Energized

One of the easiest, quickest and most convenient ways to detox is by taking deep, slow and deliberate breaths. The oxygen we take in helps clear our heads, slow down our heart rate, and help us relax again. Plus by shifting your awareness on your breathing, you will take the focus off of toxic thoughts, people, places and habits. Start out slowly and adjust the counts to your comfort level.

1. Find a place to sit down comfortably

2. Take a nice deep breath in through your nose to a count of four.

3. Hold for a count of six.

4. Breathe out through your mouth for a count of eight.

5. Start by doing this two to three times. If you start to feel a bit lightheaded, stop and breathe as you normally do. With practice increase to four or five repetitions. Do this several times a day and become aware of the combined relaxation and new energy you will experience.

CHAPTER TWO

GOOD STRESS /BAD STRESS

"Are you a good witch or a bad witch?"

In my office in Princeton, N.J., I have a tea mug that asks the key question, "Are you a good witch or a bad witch?" The tea mug also has a picture of dear Glenda the good witch of the South. Whenever I see this tea mug, I can hear Glenda's high pitch good natured voice, and that makes laugh. This reminds me to ask, whenever I find myself faced with a potential toxic person, place or situation, is this *really* a bad thing or a good thing? Who is in control here?

Stop for a moment and let's go back a bit. Why should we determine if something is good or bad? After all, we encounter *bad witch* toxins inside and out of our bodies all of the time. People are known to live long healthy lives even though they have been exposed to toxic air, water, chemicals, people, places, etc. with no impact Some say that everyone may carry various types of cancer cells in their body all of the time and do not necessarily get cancer. Why do some people become sick and others do not? Why do some people succumb to the *bad witches* while others do not?

The toxins themselves are *not* completely to blame and do *not* dictate if we get sick. It is only when our natural defenses and immunity goes down for a prolonged period of time that these toxins start to negatively impact our body by causing stress. Prolonged exposure to toxic people, places, lifestyles or things *combined* with a reduction in our defenses and immune system bring about stress that, if not effectively stopped, may lead to pain and disease. It is important to know your sources of stress, and it is equally important to know how to boost your immunity to those things that are causing you stress.

The word stress often evokes a sense of concern and perhaps even fear. Yet, stress can be both good and bad. When we exercise a muscle, it is the added stress that causes that muscle to grow and strengthen. It is said that trees need the stress of the wind to help them grow. Plants and flowers actually come into bloom when they are stressed by temperature changes. This type of positive stress even has its own specific name-"eustress". When our own bodies are stressed, we produce all sorts of natural chemicals that improve the way we move and lead to heightened mental agility and problem solving abilities. Stress is natural and very much a needed part of life.

There is also bad stress which we know as "distress". We are quite familiar with this type of stress when we are ill, are unable to sleep, cannot think clearly, or feel immobilized due to internal and/or external stress. The important difference between eustress and distress is that prolonged distress has a very costly impact to our health and well-being. It is indeed very important to know and ask "Are you a good witch or a bad witch" in order to make choices and take appropriate action.

THE HIGH COST OF DISTRESS

Indeed, distress can affect your body, your thoughts, health and feelings, your behavior and even longevity. Being able to recognize common distress symptoms can give you a jump start on managing them. It has become widely accepted knowledge that distress that's left unchecked can contribute to health problems, such as high blood pressure, heart disease, obesity, digestion, diabetes, and more serious diseases. Prolonged distress can compromise our natural immune system and make us more prone to illnesses.

COMMON EFFECTS OF DISTRESS		
Physically	**Mentally**	**How you act/react–Your Behavior**
• Physical aches and pains • Lack of energy • Change in sex drive • Digestive problems • Poor sleep • Compromised immune system • Physical disease	• Anxiety • Fears • Restlessness • Difficulty focusing • Lack of motivation • Irritability or anger • Sadness or depression • Poor memory	• Unhealthy eating habits • Angry outbursts • Substance abuses • Smoking • Withdrawal from family and friends • Poor work or school performance • Forgetfulness

THE POWER OF BELIEF

As Henry Ford was credited as saying, "Whether you think you can or you think you can't, either way you are correct". What is so fascinating is the fact that often the same stress situation can be perceived as both good and bad by different people! For example, you are at work when at 10AM you receive an urgent e-mail that your boss wants to see you at 5:00PM. Some people react to this as negative stress and say, "Oh no, I must have done something wrong and I am going to be reprimanded or lose my job!" Other people may react to the very same e-mail and say, "Wow I must have done an awesome job on that big project and I am going to be acknowledged or may even get a bonus!" One reaction causes extreme distress for a long period of time, the other does not.

Another example is when *Jerry* and *Jan* get into an elevator and accidentally step on the shoes of a man behind them who proceeds to loudly lash out yelling about how terrible they are for stepping on his feet and ruining his shoes. *Jerry* reacts by apologizing and then feeling so upset that he can't stop thinking about this and feels terrible for the rest of his day. *Jan* turns around and apologizes to the man and then moves on with the rest of her day. Same *exact* incident, two totally different reactions. One results in distress and the other does not. Same situation and same information and yet the only thing that is different is the "meaning" or "interpretation" given by Jerry and Jan.

While we know there are distressful situations that come our way that we cannot avoid—we may get ill; we may stub our toes; we may lose a job; we may lose loved ones, it is possible to help alter the impact these situations have on our life and well-being.

- **First acknowledge the situation**. Know and understand the causes of distress in your life. *Denial* is more than a river in *Egypt*. Denial or attempting to be stoic does no good for anyone. Being open and honest is healing. I truly believe in the Biblical saying, "The truth will set you free". Hiding your head in the sand will only give you a sandy head.

- **Learn how to immunize yourself** and seek support to bolster your defenses; stay connected with others and avoid isolation. Ask for help and build your healthy support network.

- **Change the meaning you give to the situation**. Sometimes this is not possible, yet it is worthwhile to attempt to look at different possible explanations and outcomes. Remember Jerry and Jan in the elevator? Can you think outside of the box? Changing the meaning will be very empowering and give you a new strength to move onward in your life.

O.K., let's put this into action and help our subconscious receive another important "aha" moment. Each of these "aha" moments are getting you closer to your skills with hypnotic detox.

1. **Think of a distressful situation (current or past) and briefly describe it here. What person, place or thing is/has caused you distress?**

    _____

    _____

    _____

    _____

    _____

    _____

    _____

    _____

2. **How might this impact on you in terms of your body, mood and behavior?**

    _____

    _____

    _____

    _____

    _____

    _____

    _____

    _____

    _____

3. **How can you immunize yourself to this distressful situation? Where can you get support? Who can you talk to? What resources do you have?**

_____

_____

_____

_____

_____

_____

_____

_____

4. **What other meaning can you give to this potentially distressful situation? Have fun thinking outside of the usual box. If you are still stuck, ask someone else for their ideas here.**

_____

_____

_____

_____

_____

_____

_____

_____

Did you notice any shift as you completed these questions? Did the impact of this situation change for you in your mind/feelings? What are your thoughts about good stress/bad stress? Please note any "aha" moments or perceptions here. Your subconscious is hungry for this:

_____

_____

_____

_____

_____

_____

_____

_____

_____

_____

KEY TAKE AWAYS:

- Prolonged toxicity can lead to stress

- Stress can be both bad and good = Eustress vs. Distress

- Good stress is a necessary part of growth and life

- Distress can cause a serious negative impact to our body, mood and behavior.

- You can alter the impact of distress by acknowledging the situation, asking for help, connecting with others, and changing the meaning of the distressful situation.

- Always ask, "Are you a good witch or a bad witch?" and take appropriate action(s).

DETOX RECIPE #2
How to be Free of Emotional Vampires

As Tony Robbins says, "We become who we surround ourselves with." We can all benefit from the good vibes shared by people who care about us and are successful in areas that we appreciate. This is especially true when facing a distressful situation. Surround yourself with this type of positive energy. Avoid spending your time around those people who do not support you. I call these people "emotional vampires." They literally suck the life out of you and can actually add to the impact of distress.

1. Take a look at the people around you. Who are the people you associate with each day?

2. Note which people seem to "give" you energy.

3. Are there any people who seem to "zap away" your energy?

4. Are there people in your life who sincerely care about you and that you trust?

5. Where can you connect with people who can be of support to you?

6. Are there people in your life who are already successful in areas that you aspire to?

7. Where can you connect with successful people?

8. Make a conscious effort to schedule time to spend with those people who believe in you and want you to succeed.

9. What can you do to minimize or eliminate the time spent with any emotional vampires?

CHAPTER THREE

YOUR MIND WORKS FASTER THAN YOU THINK

Looking behind the Wizard's curtain –
What is this thing we call Hypnosis?

WHAT *IS* THIS THING WE CALL HYPNOSIS?

Say the word hypnosis and you are sure to get an interesting reaction. Whenever I meet someone new and they ask what my profession is, and I tell them, "I am a hypnotist", their reaction is almost universal. The first thing I notice is that they suddenly recoil a bit and avoid looking me in the eyes. It is as if they fear I have some sort of Svengali powers and can control their mind; know their deepest secrets or make them bark like a dog or quack like a duck. The conversation with most people around hypnosis is edgy at best. They will say "Oh that is interesting" and then switch topics as soon as possible. Sometimes people respond with comments like, "Does *that* really work? I don't believe in it and I don't think I can be hypnotized." Sometimes I get the ever popular response, "Can you just *do* me?" To which I jokingly respond, "So if I was a proctologist would you ask me to just *do* you?" No, as a professional hypnotist I do not *do* people. I support people and help them get their own results.

The fact is hypnosis is a very natural part of life and all of us have been hypnotized *hundreds* of times throughout our lives. Let me ask you a question, have you ever gotten into your car to drive to work or the supermarket and when you arrived had no recollection of how you got there? Driving a car is a *very* serious matter and you *should* be fully aware of each car, stop light, speed sign and road. Yet you were not consciously aware of these details. Most likely you were thinking of a conversation or something you had to do later in the day and you actually drove that car subconsciously in a hypnotic trance! Wow, so if you can drive a car in a type of hypnotic trance, just imagine what else you could do with hypnosis!

Have you ever read an intriguing book or been fully absorbed in a task on the computer that when someone repeatedly called your name you did not respond. Guess what? You were in a form of hypnotic trance and this trance caused you to genuinely stop *hearing* your name being called. Pretty strong stuff, yes?

THE FACTS AND NOTHING BUT THE FACTS ABOUT HYPNOSIS–CAN I BE HYPNOTIZED?

Simply put, my definition of hypnosis is: the process of creating a relaxed state that bypasses the critical factor (gatekeeper) of the conscious mind to engage with the subconscious, usually with the intent of creating desired change(s) and/or accessing information.

The feeling of hypnosis is similar to that of meditation with a bit of a twist. I like to say that when we meditate, we attempt to empty our mind of all conscious thoughts and outside distractions. Hypnosis is similar to this with the exception that we have new suggestions and outcomes. Hypnosis is like meditation with specific *new* directions and outcomes added.

Everyone can be hypnotized to some level or another, providing that:

a. You have the ability to focus and concentrate and have average or above intelligence.

b. You are confident and comfortable with the idea of being in hypnosis.

c. You want to be in hypnosis.

What is different is that people may go into various *states* of hypnosis. Some people (perhaps 10%) do have the ability to go into a very deep level of hypnosis while the majority of people, myself included, can go into a mild to moderate level. To achieve amazing results, it is not necessary to go into a deep state of hypnosis. Actually there is really only one thing that can keep people from being hypnotized and it is a four letter word that begins with "F": FEAR. Fear comes from a lack of knowledge and facts. Let's clear up those misconceptions and concerns and help eliminate those fears.

Here are some key questions and answers about hypnosis:

1. **Will I lose consciousness or be out of control?** No! You will not lose consciousness and you will be in complete control. While your eyes may be closed and you are relaxed, you will know that you are not unconscious or asleep. Most likely you will hear everything that is being said to you.

2. **Will I have difficulty awakening?** No! You are at all times able to awaken yourself should you wish to do so. However, it is to your advantage to remain in the hypnotic state until your hypnotist asks you to awaken.

3. **Is a weak will needed for hypnosis?** On the contrary, a strong-willed person is more likely to be successful in hypnosis. All hypnosis is really self-hypnosis. You are the "driver" and your hypnotist is simply the guide. Your hypnotist is the GPS.

4. **Can I be hypnotized against my will?** No! You are in control. You can always refuse to go into hypnosis if you so desire.

5. **While in hypnosis, can I be forced to do something against my will?** No! You will not do anything that you are against doing. This is why it is so important to take the time to carefully build the suggestions that you honestly want. I spend considerable time determining how *committed* my clients are to their suggestions as I know that these suggestions must be *congruent* to what they want. Furthermore, you will not divulge any secrets or information while in hypnosis that you do not want to share. You are in control.

6. **If I do not believe in hypnosis, will this make any difference?** You do not have to believe in hypnosis in order to go into the hypnotic state. You must, however, be willing to go along with what your hypnotist tells you.

7. **Can hypnosis harm me?** Hypnosis can do you no more harm than night-time sleep. However, be sure to work with an ethical and professional hypnotherapist who is governed by a strict code of conduct and has received approved training. Also be sure to check with any medical professional that you are currently seeing prior to starting a hypnosis program.

8. **Is it possible to hypnotize oneself?** Yes! Actually, as you will soon see in this chapter, *all* hypnosis is actually *self-hypnosis.* With a little practice you can learn to manage your own self-hypnosis. This may help you get further results.

9. **Will I remember what happened in the hypnotic state?** In general, you will be aware of all that goes on during your session. You will hear all that is being said. If you choose to go into very deep hypnosis, what went on while you were hypnotized may seem like a night-time dream. Generally while in hypnosis your level of conscious awareness goes up and down. This is similar to what you may feel while in a daydream.

10. **Should I use hypnosis for my situation?** In general there is no reason why you should not use hypnosis for your problem, but, of course, it is up to you to make the decision. If you have a severe physical or mental condition, have your hypnotist check with your medical professional first. In such cases I give my clients a referral form to be filled out prior to starting sessions. Hypnosis is not meant as a replacement for medical treatment. I want my clients to be as comfortable as possible to use hypnosis to supplement any medical treatment.

OH SO *"THAT"* IS WHAT IT IS LIKE TO BE IN HYPNOSIS!

Let's cut to the real nitty-gritty. Do you want to know what it feels like to be in hypnosis right now? Here is what I want you to do. Have someone you know and trust read the following to you:

1. Find yourself a comfortable chair to sit it.

2. Minimize any possible distractions such the phone ringing or dogs barking, etc.

3. Be sure to put your feet flat on the floor and your hands in your lap.

4. Close your eyes.

5. Take two deep breaths in through your nose, hold for a count of three and then breathe out through your mouth for a count of four.

6. Take two more deep breaths.

7. Now with your next breath, go over to the corner and stand on your head.

My guess is that you followed the first six directions beautifully and then when the last one came around you laughed and opened your eyes and thought, "What the heck?" Unless you are someone who is comfortable standing on your head, you refused and simply came out of hypnosis. This is what it is like to be in hypnosis. You hear what is being said to you, follow a few simple directions, and seem to "play along." If there is a suggestion that you are not comfortable with, you will not follow it and will most likely come out of hypnosis.

WHAT IF I GET "STUCK" IN HYPNOSIS?

No one has ever been brought to the emergency room because they were stuck in hypnosis. Even if you go into a light restful nap, you will always come out of it on your own.

ALL HYPNOSIS IS SELF-HYPNOSIS

When we look at the process of hypnosis it becomes clear that there is no "Svengali-like" effect. No one can control your mind just by using hypnosis. The reason for this is that in order to be in a hypnotic state, you must *allow* yourself to go there. You, not the hypnotist, are *always* in control. The suggestions you come up with are ones that *you* want, not those of the hypnotist. They *must* be consistent with what you want. *You* are driving the car and the hypnotist is your GPS. It is important to choose a hypnotist who has been trained as a good navigator. However, if you find you are going down a road you do not want to go to, you will immediately stop the car and get back on track.

CONSCIOUS VS. SUBCONSCIOUS–THE DYNAMIC–DUO

Our brain has a wonderful ability to process information and thoughts either consciously or subconsciously. This does not happen exclusive of each other. Each part serves specific purposes and both *must work together*. Often, when we first learn something new, we have to do this on a primarily conscious level. Think about the first time you learned how to drive a car or how a baby first starts to walk. The new process is usually slow and awkward because we are making conscious connections and efforts. It is only when the new process becomes a part of our subconscious level that it seems to naturally flow and little "thought" is needed. Remember how we can *now* get into our car and drive to a destination and not fully remember how we got there? How fascinating is it that just by the repetition of a new process through our *conscious* mind that this process becomes more natural and automatic as it is accepted by and acted upon by our *subconscious*! Each is equally important and each is very different and unique and each has specific jobs to do:

Our Conscious Mind Is:

Judgmental: It offers a clear opinion if a situation is good or bad for us.

Analytical and Rational: It applies learned logic to make a determination for us. It is called the *thinking* part of the brain.

Critical: It rationalizes and complains. It can be that little voice in your head that says, "You want to drop weight; how you expect to do it *this* time? You have tried so many times before and it *never* worked and there is no logic that says it will work this time." It prefers to keep the status quo—to keep things like they already are —with minimal changes. We call this the *critical factor* in hypnosis. It is this critical "gatekeeper" that keeps messages from going to and being acted upon by the subconscious.

The Conscious mind will think before it acts. It *looks* before it *leaps*. It is cautious, slower and more deliberate than the subconscious. It needs to fully make a judgment, to accept and understand something before moving forward. When we communicate, we generally communicate through our conscious level.

The Subconscious Mind Is:

Non-Judgmental: It lacks the ability to determine if something is good or bad.

Non Analytical: It does not use logic. It does not think, it just does.

Non-Critical: It accepts most suggestions without resistance.

The subconscious is not a child yet it often acts *childlike*. The subconscious loves us. It loves to maintain the status quo until we tell it otherwise. It lacks the judgment to know if it is doing something that is not helpful to us. It generally does whatever we tell it do to and it wants us to be happy. It will follow instructions with little, if any, questioning. It works very quickly and efficiently. For this reason it is said that our subconscious is perhaps a million times faster than our conscious. As a matter of fact, changes and actions made by our subconscious mind can happen in a nano-second. Our (subconscious) mind does, indeed, work faster than we (consciously) think.

We rely on our subconscious to take care of normal automatic body functions such as breathing, heart beating, digestion, etc. Can you imagine what it would be like if we had to rely on our conscious mind to take each and every breath or be aware of and control each heart beat? Things that we do automatically or habitually, without *thinking* are controlled by the subconscious. If we could control these things consciously, than it would be easy to stop an irrational recurring fear, stop biting our nails, eat healthier, exercise more, or change anything else that we do or want to stop or do differently but don't. When we want to make these types of changes, it is necessary to get *past* the slow and deliberate conscious "gatekeeper" or "critical factor."

KEY TAKE AWAYS:

- Hypnosis is the process of bypassing the critical factor (gatekeeper) of the conscious to communicate with the subconscious, usually to create change(s) and/or access information.

- Hypnosis is a natural process that we all have experienced throughout our life.

- Just about anyone can be hypnotized.

- A mild- to moderate level of hypnosis is often all that is needed to make major changes.

- Fear and lack of knowledge are the things that keep us out of hypnosis.

- In hypnosis you will not lose consciousness or be out of control. You will not divulge any secrets or information that you want to keep private.

- You cannot be forced into hypnosis or forced to do something you do not want to do during or post-hypnosis. You are in control.

- You will most likely hear all that happens during hypnosis.

- All hypnosis is self-hypnosis. You are always in control of the *car*.

- No one has ever been *stuck* in hypnosis. You will always come out of hypnosis safely and easily.

- The conscious mind: judgmental, analytical, critical, slower and more deliberate. The conscious is the *gatekeeper* to the subconscious. We call this the *critical factor*.

- The subconscious mind: non-judgmental, non-analytical, and noncritical. The subconscious is perhaps a million times more effective and faster than the conscious and can make changes happen in a nano-second.

- The subconscious can get stuck causing behaviors, habits and thoughts that no longer serve us. In order to bring about desired change, we must get through the gatekeeper of the conscious mind. We must be able to stop those critical and judgmental voices from the conscious that may prevent us from obtaining new results.

DETOX RECIPE #3
*How to Experience the Difference between
the Conscious and Subconscious*

You don't fully understand or accept what I am saying here about the conscious vs. subconscious? Try this easy experiment to experience firsthand the difference between the two:

1. Be sure you have a watch with a second hand on it.

2. Have someone with you who can hold the watch and time you.

3. When the other person says go, have them time you as you say all the 26 letters of the alphabet. Note how long this took.

4. Now have them time you as you say half the letters of the alphabet. If it took you twelve seconds to say all of the letters, it should take you half this time to say half the letters, right?

5. When the other person says go, say as fast as you can, every other letter.

Write down what happened.

1. **How long did it take to say all the letters? How long did it take to say half the letters? Did it take half the time to say half of the letters by skipping every other letter?**

   _____

   _____

   _____

2. **Was saying all of the letters first done consciously or subconsciously?**

   _____

   _____

   _____

3. **Was skipping every other letter a conscious or subconscious process? Why?**

    _____

    _____

    _____

    _____

    _____

4. **Which was easier? Why? Did you even *want* to finish the second task?**

    _____

    _____

    _____

5. **Can you think of other activities that you do subconsciously? How effective are you doing these? Examples: driving a car, walking, and breathing.**

    _____

    _____

    _____

    _____

We have repeated the alphabet since we were children to the point that it becomes a subconscious process that is fast, easy and automatic. In order to skip every other letter, something we don't usually do, we have to slow down and need the help of the conscious. Employing the subconscious allows us to shift gears and act quickly and effectively as long as we are clear about what it is we want to change. Sometimes repetition allows us to transition over to the subconscious. Other times we have to take a more proactive approach to by-pass the conscious mind's *gatekeeper or critical factor.*

CHAPTER FOUR

WHERE YOU LOOK IS WHERE YOU GO

"Follow the yellow brick road"

GETTING THROUGH THE GATEKEEPER–BYPASSING THE CRITICAL FACTOR

Why is it so important to get past the conscious mind's critical factor (gatekeeper)? Since the conscious mind is so logical and rational, wouldn't we want to include it with the process of making changes? This *would* be helpful if it were not for the fact that most of the things that are causing us distress and that we want to change are controlled by the subconscious ,which does not use the tactics of logic and rationalization.

We do not get rid of *irrational* fears and phobias by *consciously* asking them to go away in a logical manner.

Think of your subconscious as a *machine*, such as your car. A machine alone has no logic or judgment. When you get into your car and give a little gas and turn the steering wheel to the left, what does the car do?

51

It goes left. It does not say to you, "Do you think it is a good idea to go left today? Maybe we should go right instead? I am not sure if going left today is a good thing. Well maybe going left is a good thing, let me think it over." The car does what you tell it to do. *You* are the one in charge, and it is up to you to take care of it and see that it gets the right fuel and maintenance and updating. If your car worked *consciously*, it would have to analyze and judge each and every step. Driving would be a very slow laborious process and we would never get anywhere.

Think of another machine you use--your computer. The computer does what *you* tell it to do. It does what the programs *you* put into it has it do. If it gets stuck it does not tell us, "That old program is not useful anymore, time to update it." It is a machine that follows what you ask it to do, and it is up to you to have it updated so it will run correctly. It will follow the same program over and over again until you update it with *new* programing that better serves you.

Hypnosis, NLP, EFT/Tapping, and Aromatherapy, are all elegant ways that effectively bypass the critical factor the powerful subconscious. You are going to learn about these amazing techniques very soon! One step at a time. Each is leading you toward the next destination. Keep your sights focused ahead on the yellow brick road.

YOUR SUBCONSCIOUS LOVES YOU. IT IS STUCK BECAUSE IT JUST DOES NOT KNOW ANY BETTER...UNTIL NOW.

You have just learned that all habitual *toxic* behaviors that are now causing distress in our lives are controlled by the subconscious mind. Most of the time these same behaviors actually served a purpose for us at a time in the past--usually when we were quite young. For example, think about what it *would* be like if you were four years old, and as a prank an older sibling locked you in a dark closet that you could not escape from for over an hour. This could very well cause a strong emotional reaction such as a fear of closed spaces and/or a fear of a dark space. This could stick with you for years to come.

We call the action of being locked in the closet the *initial sensitizing event* that created an *imprint* (similar to putting a program into a computer), leading to the continued fearful responses that are repeated long into adulthood. The first responses to being locked in a dark closet as a child are very correct and served a viable purpose—the child is afraid, calls out, cries and feels helpless. He/she may even feel that his/her life is at risk. This fear and the reactions of panic and helplessness are all very real. From this point on the child responds by avoiding all small and/or dark rooms. Children are especially susceptible to having these reactions *imprint* onto their subconscious *immediately* bypassing the critical factor (gatekeeper) of the conscious mind. These initial incidents happen quickly and are linked with strong *emotional* responses that go right to the subconscious. There is no time for the conscious mind to analyze the situation with logic and prevent it from entering into the subconscious.

Then the child grows up. The imminent danger and experience of being locked in a dark closet has long since passed and yet the now older and wiser adult seems stuck with the same fears. These fears are continually distressful. Although the reality of the fear is gone, the emotional reactions the subconscious continues to have holds this now adult back from living his/her life fully. Adults that have been traumatized as children may have a difficult time doing ordinary things, i.e., they may not be able to ride an elevator, or they cannot be in a car, or they cannot be outside late at night. The subconscious does not hold onto these fears and responses to *punish* us, rather, our subconscious really *loves* us. The subconscious is just stuck and lacks any judgment to view its actions and reactions as good or bad. It does what it was told to do, no matter how long ago, until we get in there to thank it and offer new behaviors that will better serve us. By using hypnosis we are able to bypass the critical factor (gatekeeper) of the conscious mind to talk directly to the subconscious and explain specifically what changes are *now* needed.

I often use this metaphor with my clients. I tell them that these habits are similar to the fact that when we were very, very young, we all needed diapers. The diapers certainly served a necessary and important purpose. Yet, when we grew up the *diapers* were no longer needed. I help my clients work through what emotional diapers they are still using that are no longer needed and teach them how to communicate with their subconscious to eliminate these *diapers* and move on.

Can you take a moment now and write down what emotional diapers you may have been carrying in your life that are no longer helpful to you? What are the *thoughts* and *reactions* to food, fears, habits, people or other situations that may have once helped you long ago but no longer serve you? How were they once of service to you?

_____

_____

_____

_____

_____

_____

How is this holding you back? What reactions in your life made sense once and now need to change? What would letting go of these emotional *diapers* do for your life?

_____

_____

_____

_____

_____

_____

_____

So now that you know which emotional *diapers* you no longer want, how do you go about making changes? The first step is to determine what you want.

WHAT DO YOU WANT...NOT WHAT YOU "DON'T" WANT

The language of the subconscious is very specific and different from the language of the conscious. For example, the subconscious does not understand the use of negatives. This includes words such as, *no, not, un–, stop, no longer.*

Let me give you an example with this fun experiment that you can do with another person. Ask the other to do the following:

1. Take a nice deep breath in through his nose and exhale through his mouth.

2. Ask him to close his eyes.

3. Now say to him, "Whatever you do, do *NOT* think of a purple cow! Do *NOT* think of a purple cow with pink polka dots on it."

4. Have him open his eyes, and ask what happened.

Most likely when you asked him to *not* think of the purple cow he started to laugh and found that he could not stop thinking of the purple cow with or without pink polka dots. This is because the vast majority of us are wired this way. In order to *not* do something, we first have to think about what it is we do not want to do. We have to go inside and picture or imagine the thing that is to be negated. For this reason, the subconscious does not understand the commands of "stop eating these foods," "don't be afraid of elevators, " "undo the anger I am feeling,";" I no longer want to crave cigarettes." If anything, when these negative words are used, the result is the subconscious will do the opposite of what is asked of it. It will experience the area that we want it *not to do.* If we say, "Don't think about smoking that cigarette," the subconscious has to go inside the mind and first figure out what is like to smoke that cigarette: the exact opposite of what is wanted.

How this translates into hypnosis and devising effective suggestions is that we want to come up with wording about what we want, not what we *do not* want. The problem is that too many people know easily what they do not want--they don't want to smoke, they want to stop craving unhealthy foods, they don't want to fear elevators. People have difficulty sharing with the subconscious what they *do* want. They get stuck. They sit in their car and say, "I don't want to go left today." So by not offering new directions to the car, you get stuck sitting in a car that goes nowhere. The subconscious needs to be told exactly *what* to do and be given doable steps. We need to get in the car, give a little gas, and turn the steering wheel right if we now want to go right instead of left.

The following exercise will help you get clarity and help you focus on what you *want*, NOT what you do *not want*.

1. **Write down something that you no longer want to do or want to change, such as to stop craving cigarettes or eating unhealthy foods or to no longer be fearful of something.**

   _____

   _____

   _____

2. **Now write down what you want instead and provide as much detail as possible. The subconscious loves details. For example, "I eat healthy foods in healthy amounts." Be sure to avoid words such as stop, end, no longer, and so on. You will get nowhere by saying I *don't* want to go left. Instead say I *want* to go right.**

   _____

   _____

   _____

3. **Now take that description of what you want, and make it even more *vivid*. The subconscious loves this! Here is an example I use with clients, "I eat foods such as beautifully colored fruits and vegetables, and my favorite drink is cool, clear water. I love the way all of the purple and green and yellow and orange foods look like, and I adore how fresh and clean they feel when I put them in my mouth. The sound that fresh foods make when I bite into them makes me very happy."**

_____

_____

_____

_____

_____

If you did this, great! You are on your way! You are developing your own hypnosis suggestions, ones that are sure to get results. If you skipped this **STOP** and go back and do this right **now**.

When exploring hypnosis with my clients, often I find the "area" that they initially say they *think* they need to change is not actually the "area" they *really* want to change. People often confuse strategies with outcomes. For example we may say we *think* we want to drop 30 pounds (strategy), when what we *really* want in life is to gain *significance* and make a *difference* in the world (outcome). Inevitably we may follow a change in diet and exercise and begin to drop a few pounds. After a few weeks we seem to get stuck and stop dropping weight or sabotage our weight change efforts.

By asking the right questions, it is possible to see that dropping weight did not bring about the real desired result of feeling *significant* and *making a change in the world*. If strategies are not congruent with or linked to our ultimate desires and outcomes, the strategy will be quickly dropped. This is why most New Year's resolutions fail after a few weeks. The major learning here is to be clear about what you really want and not confuse this with a potential strategy that will not give you what you want.

Here is an easy way of differentiating between the two. A *strategy* is always a *verb* or set of verbs such as: want/need to lose weight, stop craving cigarettes, desire to get a better night's sleep, become free from a fear that is holding you back. An outcome is always a *noun* or set of nouns, such as love, significance, peace, power, comfort, mental stimulation, etc.

Until you uncover what you truly want, initiating a viable strategy is almost impossible. When you clearly uncover your true desires and real outcomes--the true driving force, developing strategies becomes almost second nature. So how do you discover your outcomes?

This is easy: simply, ask. You can ask, "What is it I truly want?" and then allow yourself to be silent as this question is processed. Learn to become comfortable in the silences. Your brain needs time to think this through. Start writing down all that you want until you get to the key noun(s) that are your basic human wants/desires.

The next step is to acknowledge the importance of this need and then ask, when you think about (your outcome), what comes to mind? Let the ideas flow. What does it mean to you to have peace, for example? What do you hear, see or feel when you think of *peace*? What ideas or activities give you peace? What can you do, that you are not doing now, that would give you *peace*?

Always keep your focus on the underlying outcome you want, and draw connections to it by trying new strategies. If your outcome is love and connection, and you are also trying to drop weight, how can you link the two? Perhaps you can see that by dropping weight and being more physically active you will gain the confidence and energy you need to help you go out and do the things that will put you in contact with others. Always link your ultimate outcome with your strategies, and if the strategies are not working, change them.

HOW TO TALK SO THAT YOUR OWN SUBCONSCIOUS WILL LISTEN

Here are the main language aspects that are needed to bypass the critical factor (gatekeeper) while communicating with the subconscious:

- **Avoid using those negative words:** *stop, no longer, don't or even quit.* Focus on what you *want*, not what you *don't want*.

- **Use the present tense with your desired suggestions.** The subconscious loves to keep things as is, and if you say you *already* have the changes you want, the subconscious will do everything to keep this going. If you say "I *feel great* (present tense) eating fresh healthy foods and I crave fresh colorful fruits and vegetables in healthy amounts," the subconscious will support every opportunity to keep this going.

- **Be specific.** The subconscious needs clear directions.

- **Use fun and emotional language.** Rather than say "every morning I go to the gym to work out," the subconscious would love to hear you say "every morning my gym goddess jumps out of bed to have an energy blasting time at the gym!"

- **Reward your subconscious.** The subconscious is not a child, and yet it acts a bit childlike. It loves to be rewarded when it does all of those new behaviors that you want. Plan for success and reward all positive changes- large and small. Discover ways to immediately reward yourself (and your subconscious) that are constructive, easy and fun. It could be as simple as doing a happy dance each time you notice a new, positive change. Whatever reward you choose, be sure that it is *congruent* with the *new* behavior.

How will you reward your subconscious when it starts making changes? Who can you celebrate with? Try these: make a high-five; do a happy dance; have tea with a friend; spend a day at a spa. Write some other ways you would acknowledge success:

_____

_____

_____

_____

KEY TAKE AWAYS:

- Most of the things you want to change are controlled by the programs that are stuck in your subconscious mind.

- The subconscious acts like a machine that needs to be clearly told what to do and where to go. It will keep going in the same direction until you tell it to change direction with clear language and suggestions that it can understand.

- Hypnosis, language patterns such as those used in N.LP., Tapping, Aromatherapy, and other key modalities will help you get through the conscious mind's gatekeeper/critical factor.

- Focus on where you want to go. Avoid using words such as stop, no longer, no, quit, as these do not tell the subconscious *what you want*—only *what you don't want*.

- Make your suggestions specific and in the present tense--as if this is already happening.

- The strategies you use (verbs) will only be acted upon it they are clearly linked to your outcomes (nouns).

- Make your suggestions fun and colorful: the subconscious is not a child, and yet it often responds to things in a childlike manner.

- Be sure to come up with easy rewards whenever your childlike subconscious completes new behaviors.

DETOX RECIPE #4
How to Create a Positive and Creative State of Mind

In addition to breathing, the most immediate thing we can do to shake free from stagnation is to **move**. Motivational speaker, Tony Robbins, refers to this as "physiology first" and I think this is a very good mantra indeed. Just as our mind can create physical responses in our body. For example, if we have a fear of spiders and someone says there is a spider nearby (real or not), our body will respond physically with shorter breathing, elevated heart rates, face flushing and the emotion of fear. The amazing thing is that the opposite is true too. Our physical body can alter how we think. Here is a recipe for you to follow to show the power of simple physiology to change the way you think and feel and how to use this to create a positive creative state.

Go through this process and allow your body to mimic each of these changes. Write down what you notice:

1. Think of someone who is sad, lonely and afraid- what would this person look like in the mirror?

2. How does their posture and back look?

3. How are they holding their shoulders?

4. Imagine how you would be standing?

5. What would your face look like?

6. Would you be looking up or down?

7. What do the muscles around your eyes and mouth look like?

8. How are you breathing?

9. How does this make you feel?

Write down what you noticed and what your strategies are to create this state:

_____

_____

_____

_____

_____

_____

_____

_____

_____

Now try this out:

1. Imagine you are feeling strong; confident; carefree; courageous. Breathe the way you would breathe and look the way you would look with these feelings.

2. What would you look like now?

3. How is your posture?

4. Where are your shoulders?

5. How are you standing—where are your feet?

6. What does your face look like?

7. Where are you looking now? Up/Down?

8. How do your eyes and mouth look?

9. How is your breathing now?

10. How are you feeling now?

Write down what you noticed and what your strategies are to create this state:

_____

_____

_____

_____

_____

_____

_____

_____

_____

_____

Now think about how quickly it took to go from one state to another—a few seconds perhaps or as long as it took to read the directions. You can alter your mental state as quickly as you alter your physical body. If you get stuck or in a rut, change your physiology— if you are sitting, get up and move around, go for a walk or run. If you are at home – dance!

The power of a smile: When we make our face smile, chemicals are sent from our brain throughout our body which actually help to change our mental state. The same is true when we make ourselves frown. Whenever possible, appropriate and when you have a choice- smile. Create those happy-feeling hormones that do a body good.

Mimic the look of someone who is upbeat, confident, creative, and happy. Memories and mental states are stored in our body. By accessing cues from our physical body we can have a big immediate impact on creating the desired state. There is a lot of validity to the phrase, "fake it until you make it". Even if you don't feel upbeat right now, smile, laugh, sing, keep your focus upwards, stand up straight, take deep breaths, *pretend* with your body and your mind will *follow*.

Physical actions in our body create specific chemical responses. Think about this, if you accidentally stub your toe, (a physical action), your body produces all sorts of inner chemical and neurological responses that result in increased blood flow, color changes, inflammation and *feelings* of pain. Pretty sophisticated stuff here. It is nice to know you can create very eloquent internal changes—no need to stub your toe.

CHAPTER FIVE

THE POWER OF FOOD

"The deadly poppy field"

YOU ARE WHAT YOU EAT... FOODS THAT CAN ADD TO TOXIC DISTRESS

A book discussing *detox* must also look at the area of foods and how foods directly impact our health physically and mentally. In terms of toxic distress, it is important to understand how certain foods create a natural fight or flight response in our body. These foods cause an increase in adrenaline, cortisol and epinephrine, three very strong chemicals which originally were used by our ancestors to fiercely fight or run away from life threatening dangers such as battles with sabre tooth tigers. These chemicals work by taking the focus and circulation away from our center core – especially the areas of digestion and elimination. These areas slow down so that our extremities- head, legs and arms and heart rate have added strength, agility and energy to either fight or run away from a battle. This is actually a good thing. Even in today's world, our body may, at times, need the added strength and focus to make quick physical changes. We need the flight response to run away from a fire and we need the fight response to bolster our strength if we are in an accident.

While these responses can be lifesaving, the chemicals produced during fight or flight can stay in our body long after the danger is gone. Too often *we experience* the fight or flight response for situations that do not require it. We get overly upset at something we cannot control—just like being locked in traffic when we need to get somewhere quickly. Or we get stuck in a fear, such as public speaking, that can gnaw at us for days. Just a puff of adrenaline will stay with us for six hours or more. Here is the point, prolonged or repeated exposure to adrenaline, cortisol and epinephrine become toxic to us. These chemicals are actually referred to as stress hormones. Prolonged or repetitive exposure to these stress hormones is not a good thing and can cause all of the toxic distress responses listed in the chart in Chapter Two. Be aware that certain foods can cause an increase in stress hormones and/or they may keep these stress hormones at high levels for *prolonged* periods of time.

Take a moment and write down situations from your everyday life where you may have created a fight or flight response. For example, dealing with your boss asking you on Friday to work over the weekend, or waiting forever for the subway only to be squished inside a packed train.

_____

_____

_____

_____

_____

_____

_____

As you go back to those situations, how did your body feel- what was your breathing like? How long did these feelings stay in your body? Were you in control of your body and feelings inside? Did you feel empowered or disempowered?

_____

_____

_____

_____

_____

_____

_____

_____

Most likely the fight or flight responses you had were not very empowering or positive memories. Knowing about foods that may contribute to the extended fight or flight response could be very helpful—especially if you know you are about to face a battle with your modern day sabre tooth tiger. Here is a list of foods that you may want to avoid. Some of these items you may already be aware of, while others may offer you a new "aha". Short term many of these food substances may seem to energize you, and just as Dorothy in the Poppy Field, ultimately they will slow you down, blur your thoughts, limit your awareness and effectiveness and zap away your energy and life forces.

Caffeine: coffee; chocolates; certain herbal remedies that contain natural versions of caffeine; most energy drinks and commercial sodas. Know that not all food labels list items that are high in caffeine as caffeine. If you are sensitive or allergic to caffeine it is important to know what you are drinking/eating. Here are a few examples of hidden names for caffeine courtesy of Caffeineinformer.com.

FOOD LABEL INGREDIENT	SYNONYMS OR OTHER NAMES
Coffee Beans	Caffea sp., green coffee extract, coffee extract
Cocoa	Cacao, Theobroma cacao, chocolate, dark chocolate, cocoa nibs, cocao nibs
Kola Nut	Cola nitida, Cola Seeds, natural cola flavor
Yerba Mate'	Mate', Ilex paraguariensis
Guarana	Paullinia cupana
Green Tea	Camellia Sinesis, Thea Sinesis, Camellia, green tea extract
Black Tea	Camellia Sinesis, Thea Sinesis, Camellia, black tea extract
White Tea	Camellia Sinesis, Thea Sinesis, Camellia
Oolong Tea	Camellia Sinesis, Thea Sinesis, Camellia
Kombucha 1,3,7-trimethylxanthine	Fermented tea
Guayusa	Ilex guayusa
Yaupon	Yaupon Holly, Cassina, Ilex vomitoria
Dicaffeine Malate	Caffeine combine with malic acid
Caffeine Citrate	Caffeine combined with citric acid

Sugar: Did you know that the average American consumes over 160 pounds of sugar a year….and this rate is rising!! If you could pick only one food substance to eliminate to rid toxins in your body it would be this one, along with its cousin, artificial sweeteners. Besides empty calories, sugar adds pounds to our body and may bring on added inflammation and illness. It is also true that foods high in sugar, any type of sugar, can cause the body to shift into a fight or flight state. These foods cause the heart to race and energy levels to go from one extreme to another which is not something that would be helpful when we want to calm our nerves and overcome our fears. There really are no "safe" forms of sugar—especially if we are working to calm our nerves. Sugars can cause our blood sugar levels to increase and then drop too abruptly impacting our physical and mental energy levels. Furthermore, sugars are highly acidic which has its own issues in terms of our teeth and digestive system. Best bet is to stay away from added sugar in any form—especially when we think we may become anxious. When picking fruits, moderation is key. It is best to eat the fruit whole and avoid highly sugary fruit juices. When buying foods, read the label. Usually any substance that ends in "alose" = sugar.

For a list of 57 different names used for sugar on food labels, please see Prevention Magazine: http://www.prevention.com/food/healthy-eating-tips/57-names-sugar?s=1

Artificially decaffeinated coffees and teas: Did you know that even teas and coffees that are decaffeinated can still have the same impact as the real thing? There are no healthy beverages that can be 100% decaffeinated. Sometimes the process used to decaffeinate a beverage involves the adding of unhealthy and even caustic substances that we would want to avoid. It is best to use the highest quality teas and coffees that are preferably grown organic. Just about all teas contain caffeine. However, high quality teas contain a substance that actually helps regulate the caffeine and adds calming properties.

Artificial sweeteners: There have been many studies to show that even with artificial sweeteners, our body may still respond as if we are consuming pure sugar. Artificial sweeteners create even worse problems for us and impact our metabolism, headaches, and immune system. It is best to avoid artificial sweeteners for maximum health.

Salt: We get plenty of salt/sodium from the foods we eat. Adding additional salt will only cause the heart to speed up and add to anxiety.

When dealing with a fear it is best to keep added salt/sodium intake to a minimum and to get our needs met through natural foods. Here is a good rule of thumb, the salt/sodium content should not be higher than the calories per serving amount. If the calorie per serving estimate is 200 calories, then the salt/sodium content per serving should be at or under this number as well.

Animal Products –While meat and other animal products are a source of protein; they are not a source of viable fuel and are very challenging to the digestive tract resulting in acidic ph. These foods can add to the physical stress to the body. For full information around this area, I highly recommend that you go to www.ChristinaCooks.com for recipes and amazing resources.

...AND YOU BECOME WHAT YOU ASSIMILATE

We can have the best possible sources of food in the universe, and yet if we are in excess toxic distress and in that fight or flight state, our body will not be able to digest and assimilate needed nutrients. Remember that the stress hormones brought on by fight or flight take the focus away from our digestion. In doing this it actually slows digestion down. Also when we are in toxic anxiety, we often loose the urge to eat all together. To put it simply, if we do not eat or we are not able to digest our foods, we will become ill. Healthy digestion leads to a healthy body and mind.

It is usually best to eat lightly cooked foods to help ease our digestion and keep things moving along. For many people too many raw foods may be difficult to fully digest and eating foods that are overly cooked may lack nutritional value. When we are preparing to ease our moods it is best to eat slowly with no distractions. Eat smaller meals more often and be sure to drink water— room temperature is best. Eat more low sugar fruits such as berries and tart apples and increase your supporting veggies.

Also consider avoiding foods that can really stress the digestive system such as anything that is highly acidic, overly spicy, fried, highly processed, and contains added oils/grease. To help with digestion be sure to eat slowly and really chew your food. I work with my clients to put their forks or spoons down between each bite of food and to chew really well. It is amazing how yummy your food will taste when you do this. I even give my clients a few sets of chopsticks to help them slow down and enjoy each bit of food. If possible avoid eating out too often (as you never really know what is in prepared foods) and do more fun and healthy cooking at home. This is a great way to relax and take back more control of your life.

THERE IS NO-ONE-SIZE-FITS-ALL DIET

During my studies at the Institute for Integrative Nutrition, I learned about literally hundreds of diets. I looked at the components and impacts on the body of everything from Low Protein, High Protein, Low Carbs, High Carbs, Low Calorie, Low Fat, and High Fat, — everything under the sun, and I continue to examine these on an on-going basis. I have learned that everyone is unique and no two people respond to diets in the same way. Foods that may work for one person may not work for another person. Furthermore, the term *diet* does not serve us. A *diet* is restrictive and unyielding and virtually impossible to maintain long-term.

What does work is to experiment with different foods and notice what foods work and what foods do not work for *you*. Keep a food journal and write down everything you eat and when. Note how you feel physically and mentally one to two hours later. With these findings create a list of foods that you *choose* to eat because they taste good and make you feel good. Obviously stay clear from foods that you have an allergy to or are sensitive to. An allergic reaction can cause life threatening responses in the body. A food sensitivity may be far more subtle, but long-term they cause inflammation and related toxic distress.

There are several key points about food that are beneficial to everyone. Above all enjoy the process of eating and eat the best quality of foods available. Eat slowly with no distractions. Drink lots of good quality, clear water. Whenever possible prepare your own foods. Eat lots of the fruits and veggies that work with your specific body. How we eat and what foods we put into our digestive system impact how we assimilate nutrients which also helps determine our ability to deal with distress and help our body combat and eliminate toxins. These steps must be consistent and doable for a lifetime. There is no quick solution or magic bullet.

Personally, I do not believe in a massive change to or elimination of foods such as in radical detox for a specified period of time. In my practice I have seen too often the results of these types of detoxes. Some people initially may feel better and yet inevitably after the detox has ended, most people feel worse than before. Furthermore, I strongly say that if you are suffering from a major condition in which you are in a weakened state of health, do *NOT* do a radical restrictive detox unless advised to do so by a medical professional.

KEY TAKE AWAYS:

- Know that there are foods that may increase anxiety and create or prolong the fight or flight response.

- Prolonged or repeated exposure to the fight or flight stress hormones of cortisol, epinephrine, adrenalize can slow down digestion and cause major toxic distress in the body.

- It is important to take ownership of what you are putting in your body. Look for the hidden substances that are harmful and be sure to read all food labels to avoid these items.

- Wean yourself away from caffeinated supplements and beverages.

- Know that foods that end in "alose" = sugar and that fruit juices are extremely high in added and unnecessary sugars

- The salt/sodium number on the food label should be equal to or less than the calories number per serving.

- Avoid heavy foods that may be more difficult to digest. Eat slowly; drink cool (not cold) water; give yourself time to digest your food.

- There is no one food diet that fits all. Keep a food journal to note what you eat and how this impacts you physically and mentally one to two hours later.

- Avoid radical food detox plans unless instructed to do so by your medical professional

- Avoid distractions such as TV and loud noises when eating.

- Enjoy eating the best foods available and enjoy lots of high quality clear water.

- Experiment with cooking at home. Preparing our own food is a very empowering experience. When you prepare your own food you are in control of exactly what you eat and the process of cooking and this has a wonderful impact on our well-being. If the foods you made didn't turn out exactly as you planned, or your "audience" is hesitant to try something new, just smile and say to whomever you are cooking for, "I made this with a lot of love for you".

DETOX RECIPE #5
How to Make the Easiest Inoculating Soothing Nourishing Empowering Fortifying Detox Soup #1

The best thing we can do to make all the toxins in the world stop and allow our health, vitality and power come together is to prepare our own food. Often when I come home and don't have a clue as to what to eat, I immediately boil a big pot of water. I know I can use this to make rice, pasta, grains, etc. When even this seems like too much, I make a wonderful and easy bowl of soup. You can cut up all of the veggies the night before to make it even easier. I can have this soup morning, noon or night and I love it during any season. When I make this soup it helps me feel like I can take on the world! This makes enough for 2 cups. Feel free to double or triple it as needed.

Ingredients:

1 small onion – chopped into small chunks

1 good size carrot – chopped into small pieces

1 stalk celery – chopped into small pieces

You can add a bit of garlic powder (1/4 teaspoon) or 1-2 cloves of fresh minced garlic for added taste and nutritional value.

2-3 dried shitake mushrooms soaked in enough water to cover (soak for ½ hour, although shitakes have a mind of their own and will determine on their own when they are soaked enough. For this reason I may soak them in the refrigerator overnight).

Cut up sea veggies of your choice for added flavor and minerals. (I usually use a handful of wakame cut up into small pieces)

2-3 cups of organic veggie broth or high quality water

½ cup of firm tofu, water pressed out and cut into small ½ inch chunks

1 Tablespoon of high quality miso—I prefer white miso for this recipe

Directions:

1. Wash and chop veggies. Only peel them if they are not organic.

2. Get your sauce pot very hot (do not use a pot with non-stick surfaces, stainless steel or cast iron is best)

3. When a few drops of water added to pot "dance" when added, your pot is ready

4. Add the cut onion and stir for approximately 5 minutes. The natural water content means you do not need to use oil.

5. Next add the carrots for a few minutes. You may need to add a bit of broth or water.

6. Now add the celery and add a bit of broth or water if needed to help deglaze the pot.

7. Lower the heat to medium Add the remaining broth or water along with the water used to soak the shitake mushrooms.

8. Add the tofu and sea veggies and garlic power or minced garlic

9. Allow to cook with a low boil for another 5 minutes.

10. Turn off the heat and use a bit of the broth in small bowl to dissolve the miso. Good quality miso has live probiotics and too much high heat will alter these.

Feel free to experiment with different veggies and spices. Enjoy as you become aware of the soothing power entering your body!

How to Make the Really Easiest Inoculating Soothing Nourishing Empowering Fortifying Detox Soup #2

O.K., let's admit it, there are times when we are already carrying the weight of the world on our shoulders and the thought of cooking has the appeal of getting a root canal. When this happens, here is the easiest detox soup recipe I know of. Try it out and let me know what you think. This makes enough for 2 cups. Feel free to double or triple as needed.

Ingredients:

1 can of no salt added organic soup of your choice. I really like Hidden Valley Salt Free Tomato Soup

2 big handfuls of baby spinach washed and torn into bite size pieces

2 deep soup bowls

Added spices that you like. I add a few pinches of granulated garlic and ½ tablespoon of dried onion flakes

Directions:

1. Open the can(s) of soup and place in a pot on the stove

2. Heat gradually and add the spices you like (granulated garlic and dried onion flakes) If you decide to use fresh spices, add them towards the very end.

3. Allow the soup to come to a gentle boil for a few minutes.

4. In the meantime, add the washed and torn spinach to the bottom of each bowl.

5. Pour the hot soup over the torn spinach in the bowl.

6. Eat and enjoy! I love the combination of the creamy soup and the crunchy spinach. Feel free to use kale, collard greens or any combination for a soothing and healthy meal.

CHAPTER SIX

THE POWER OF E.F.T.

"Just click your ruby red slippers three times..."

HOW MUCH *ECSTASY* CAN YOU STAND?

I am amazed at how many of my clients think that the ability to *change* has to take a long, long time and cost a lot of money. They try to eliminate fears and phobias by spending thousands of dollars on prescribed medications and doctors' visits for years and years, only to have little, if any, results. They usually seek me out as a *last* resort after struggling with so many other therapies that simply do not work. One key tool that I help them use is Emotional Freedom Technique (E.F.T.). This is a non-invasive, and easy process to learn. It can be done virtually at any time and at any place and can reverse unresourceful states such as fears, cravings, discomfort and much more, in a matter of a few minutes. I am not suggesting that E.F.T. be used as a substitute for standard medical protocols, rather I suggest that it be used in *conjunction* with medical practices. Slowly and happily I am seeing more of this combination take place in the medical field.

Know that it is not a question about "Can I feel better?" You have it within you right now to make eloquent changes that will delight you. By using E.F.T. along with hypnosis and other easy techniques that you are finding in this book, you will instead have to ask, "Just how *much* ecstasy can I stand!" Furthermore, you will find with great happiness that change can happen very quickly indeed. You already know that your heart rate and adrenaline can shoot up in a matter of seconds if there is a perceived danger—real or imagined. Understand that you can also reverse this and create a feeling of calmness and peace in an equally fast time frame.

All of my clients are taught E.F.T. along with several methods of self-hypnosis. My personal belief is that E.F.T., while not an exact form of hypnosis, is a wonderful tool that helps us bypass that critical factor (gatekeeper) to get through to our subconscious to bring about change. These tools are to be used prophylactically, that is to say in a preventative and protective manner. I like to say that we should *kill* the *monster* while it is still *tiny*. Don't allow a fear or toxic reaction grow to the point that it is overwhelming and overpowering. As soon as you begin to feel the slightest knot in your stomach, or heart racing, use these tools. When we use these tools as soon as we feel the slightest bit of distress response from a pending person, place or situation, the toxic distress will be highly reduced or even eliminated in a matter of a few minutes.

On a personal note, if I had to pick one single technique that helped me get to the other side of my own *monster*, a life-long fear of public speaking, it would be this very same E.F.T., also known as *tapping*. I have to admit that I was very suspicious when I was first introduced to E.F.T. eight years ago by my very good friend, Nurse Patricia Crilly. However, when I saw her use this to help a six year old in the middle of a coughing fit, I was totally baffled at the immediate results. Very young children and animals do not, I believe, understand the impact of the placebo effect. Either something is really going to work for them or it is not. I then gave it a try several years back for my own fear of public speaking and found that it is easy to do; it works quickly; and it has long-term results. Within a week of using the tapping, I was virtually free of my fears and I went on to speak on stage in New York City, at Lincoln Center in front of over sixteen hundred people. What is more impressive is that I began to love public speaking and I soon became a public speaking junkie!

For a look at the specifics, I want to thank my good friend, Nurse Patricia Crilly, who has given me permission to share with you aspects of her book, *Tap it and Zap it, A Grownups Guide to EFT for Children* available on Amazon.Com as a Kindle book. Please note that the comments that are made in conjunction to the limbic system and stimulation to the brain are strictly my thoughts and these comments have no direct connection with traditional E.F.T.

E.F.T. is founded upon the belief that negative emotions are the result of a disruption in the flow of the body's energy. Following is a brief history and overview of the body's energy system. For me this means that negative or unresourceful states of mind show up as patterns that get stuck in our body. Classically, E.F.T. utilizes the energy pathways that run throughout our body known as meridians. The flow of energy (Chi) through these pathways help keep us in balance and healthy. Disruptions in these pathways impact the flow of Chi and can result in physical and emotional disruptions.

In terms of Western medicine, it is my *personal* belief that much of the area where we get emotionally *stuck* is connected closely to the limbic area of our brain. This is the area that controls such behaviors as fears, memories, cravings and other primitive responses. Our brain often cannot consciously handle being stimulated by too many things at the same time. When we use E.F.T., we *overstimulate* the brain with the senses of sight, touch, and hearing. This very effectively shuts down or restarts the limbic system thus eliminating the thought patterns and actions that were holding us back.

Specifically E.F.T. was developed by Gary Craig, a Stanford educated engineer. His work is based on the findings of Dr. Roger Callahan, a Clinical Psychologist, whose research resulted in the development of Thought Field Therapy™. Gary Craig took the concepts of Dr. Callahan and made them user friendly so that anyone could do this.

E.F.T. can be helpful for just about anything. A partial list of possibilities includes anger, anxiety, disappointment, fears and phobias, grief, guilt, improved study habits, low self-esteem, physical discomfort, road rage, sadness, sports improvement, and enhanced work and school performance. The list is endless.

HOW DOES TAPPING (E.F.T.) WORK?

In essence, E.F.T. it is an emotionally based version of acupuncture except that the needles aren't necessary. Instead, one simply "tunes in" to the emotional issue while stimulating various stress relief points along the energy meridians by "tapping" on them with the fingertips.

This provides a "balancing effect" that replaces emotional/physical distress with calm and comfort. There are a few other seemingly odd but very effective activities to go along with the tapping that complete the process. All of these activities serve to awaken the nervous system and engage the left and right sides of the brain.

E.F.T. in no way replaces traditional medical care. It is not a cure all but rather a tool to help bring about healing. It is a wonderful adjunct to standard medical care.

HERE ARE THE STEPS FOR E.F.T.:

1. **Know** the specific underlying issue. For example, Fear of Public speaking.

2. **Rate** your current intensity of this issue on a scale of 0 – 10. 0 = no problem at all and 10 = Major extreme response.

3. Start tapping the "karate chop" area of one hand with two fingers of the other hand. While saying out loud the issue using this format: "Even though I have this fear of public speaking, I completely accept and love myself". Repeat this several times. The more vivid you can make the statement, the stronger the results. Now, I know it sounds strange admitting out loud that you have this issue, yet it is very important to bring it fully to the surface in order to *shut it down* with the next steps. The following chart and basic information about E.F.T. can be found at http://www.emofree. com/ This is the official site of E.F.T. founder, Gary Craig. Karate Chop (KC) area of one hand; and the general tapping points: TOH= Top of Head; EB = Eye Brown; SE = Side of Eye; UE= Under Eye; UN = Under Nose; Ch = Chin; CB = Collar Bone; UA = Under Arm

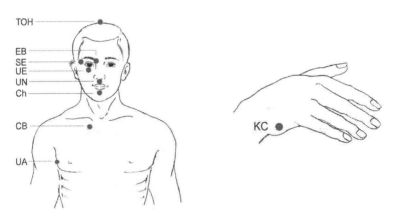

4. Next move on to each of the points shown above and as you tap several times, say out loud statements such as a) "This fear of public speaking" (EB point); b) "I don't think I can change it" (SE), c) "This fear is overwhelming" (UE), d) "I can't speak in front of others" (UN), e) "The fear" (Ch), f) "I No one is interested in what I have to say" (CB), g) "This fear of Public Speaking" (UA), h) "I can't get over it" (TOH).

5. Shake your body out and take several breaths

6. Next do another round of the points in step 4 and this time repeat the following words out loud as you tap several times: "Public Speaking", "I can do this", "People want me to succeed", "I love to share what I have to say", "I see myself succeeding and enjoying the process", "It feels great to speak in front of others", "I love public speaking", "I feel on top of the world when I am in front of others".

7. Now shake your body out and take several deep breaths.

8. Go back and access your intensity level from 0-10. How far has it gone down? Keep repeating the tapping sequence until you bring it down to a level 2 or even 0.

Understand that it is important to get the bad witch stuff out first so that you can tap the second round to make the changes wanted. It may seem counterintuitive or a bit awkward at first, give it a try and notice the changes that happen on both a mental and physical level.

KEY TAKE AWAYS:

- Emotional Freedom Technique (E.F.T.), often know as *Tapping,* is another way of breaking free from toxic thoughts, people, or situations.

- E.F.T. works by unblocking energy (Chi) pathways where these toxins get stuck in our system.

- There is a lot of validity in the saying, "The truth will set you free". Get in touch with what you are dealing with, bring this to the surface and them shut them down.

- A recap of the Tapping process can be found in Chapter 8.

DETOX RECIPE #6
How to Recognize a Bad Toxic Witch
from a Good Supportive Witch

From previous chapters, we know that the very same toxic thoughts, people or situations can cause totally different responses within different people. Much has to do with the meaning we give to these toxins. Sometimes we can eliminate a seemingly toxic witch easily on our own. For example, we can alter the initial toxic witch frustration of being stuck in traffic each day with a more supportive good witch by using this very same time to listen to music we love or even learn a new skill with an instructive cd. Other times we get stuck and need help. Either way, the first step is to detect a bad toxic witch from a good supportive witch.

In order to do this, we must first recognize the clues in our own body that are telling us when a toxic witch is about to materialize and then remember to kill the monster while it is still *small.* This recipe is intended to help you determine if/when you are coming up against a bad toxic witch that should be tapped away.

Ingredients:

A *notebook* and pen/pencil

A quiet and safe *location* with no distractions

A *memory* of a thought, person or situation that we *know* has caused us toxic distress in the past. For example the thought that we have to give a speech in a few minutes in front of a large group and we are totally unprepared….and we are very fearful of public speaking. Or if we have had, in the past an uncontrollable craving to eat an entire box of cookies that we want to avoid.

Directions:

1. Be sure to start out in a comfortable position and take a few clearing breaths.

2. Now think back to that situation, in the past, that caused you distress. Really associate to that witch. See it, feel it, hear it. What is that situation?

   _____

   _____

   _____

   _____

   _____

   _____

3. Now take a moment to check-in with yourself

4. How are you breathing?

   _____

   _____

   _____

   _____

   _____

5. How is your heart beating?

   _____

   _____

   _____

   _____

   _____

6. Where do you notice the shift or sensation in your body? Do you feel it in your stomach, chest, throat, or head?

_____

_____

_____

7. What direction is this sensation going? Clock-wise or counter-clockwise?

_____

_____

_____

8. Does this sensation have a color, sound, shape? If so what is it?

_____

_____

_____

9. What is that sensation saying to you? What words do you hear as you go back to that toxic witch? What words did you hear in the past being said to you by others?

_____

_____

_____

_____

_____

_____

Now be sure to go through and answer each of these. This is your unique key to knowing how your toxic witch operates in your world. Whenever you notice any of these changes coming on—the beating of your heart, the sensations in your body, the words you hear, etc., this is a warning to stop and use all of your tools to kill the toxic witch *monster* while it is still little. Sometimes you can even do this by simply reversing the warning signals. - Take deep breaths, reverse the direction of the sensation, change the words you hear or the colors you see that have been produced by that toxic witch.

Sounds a bit simplistic? Remember back to Chapter Four – physiology first. Your mind will respond to how you use your body. If the toxic witch makes the sensation twirl around in your stomach in a clock-wise manner, shake things up by twirling it around in a counter-clockwise direction. Don't take any crap from that witch. You take control of the situation and this becomes easier to do once you master the ability to recognize the beginnings of a toxic witch and get rid of it while it is still little. Now take a moment and just summarize what you have learned and how you are going to apply this *NOW* and going forward.

Fill in the blanks

"When I start to see, hear, and feel:"

_____

_____

_____

_____

_____

"I will *immediately* respond by doing:"

_____

_____

_____

_____

_____

CHAPTER SEVEN

PUTTING IT ALL TOGETHER

*"There's no place like home,
there's no place like home."*

SO TELL ME, WHEN WOULD *NOW* BE A GOOD TIME TO CHANGE?

Congratulations! You have successfully learned how to *detect* your own personal toxic witches that may take the form of thoughts, people and situations, and you realize the potential distress that these can do if you don't eliminate the toxins while they are still *little*. So let's talk about specific strategies to help you *detox* them out of your system once and for all, so that you can stay happy and healthy and lead the life you want to have. We have already touched upon several strategies throughout this book. Specifically you have learned to:

- Know the difference between good stress (eustress) and bad stress (distress) – Always go inside and ask in Glenda's high pitched voice, is this stress "a good witch or a bad witch" and take appropriate action(s)

- Know what thoughts, people, or situations can cause you to feel distress and how to eliminate emotional vampires

- Know the difference between the conscious mind and the subconscious mind

- Know how to use language so that the subconscious hears you

- Know how your modern day fight or flights responses can cause distress in your body

- Know which foods can bring on or extend a fight or flight response

- Know how to identify foods that work for you and ways to prepare and eat foods that support you even more

- Know the power of E.F.T. or Tapping and how to use this as a preventive inoculation against toxic distress caused by specific people, places or situations.

- Know how to sniff out a toxic witch with key signals from your body and how to reverse them to get rid of the toxic witch while it is still little.

Let's look at how you can pull this all together and even add a few more tools in your toolkit to get even stronger results. I like to call these tools my, "Secret Ninja tricks of the trade". The first key step that is necessary to change(s) is to make the *decision* and *choice* to change. You have to really *want* this. So you have to decide, when would *NOW* be a good time to change? Remember you cannot be forced to do something in hypnosis that you don't want to do. A major part of wanting change is seeing the benefit of making that change. What is the benefit to detoxing from those toxic thoughts, people, and situations to you? This is very logical. If you do not see the full value of making a change, you simply are not going to accept the changes. You must be fully congruent with the change(s) you want to make.

There are times when people come to see me and tell me they want to change, and yet deep down I can see they are holding on to the very thing they say they are wanting to change. This happens for one of two reasons. First, they really do *not* want to change. For example, someone comes in because they say they want to stop smoking. As we talk, it turns out the reason they want to stop is because someone else asked them to do so and deep down they really still enjoy smoking and don't want to stop. There is no way they will stop smoking unless they seriously want to stop for *themselves* and I will end the session because I do not want to waste their money and our time on something that will not change. I will turn away nearly half the people who come to me to stop smoking because I will only work with clients that I believe I can help.

A second situation is when someone consciously really *does* want to change, and yet deep down- perhaps subconsciously, they want to hold on to the situation because it satisfies or serves them in some key way. An example of this is a person who wants to eliminate their fear of driving. In this situation, they clearly believe they want this. They know their lives would improve if they were able to drive in terms of their work and overall freedom. As we talk further together, we find that their fear of driving has led to other behaviors that they may want to hold on to. On some level, it is nice to have other people drive them around and their fear has helped them get out of situations, such as picking family up at the airport, that they really don't like doing. We call this situation as having *secondary gains*. Not being able to drive has certainly limited their lives, yet it also gives them something back in return. In order to move on, together we unearth any secondary gains; put them into perspective and highlight the major benefits of changing the fearful behavior(s). With clients I establish this by discussing what the old toxins have cost them in their lives. Let's make sure you are congruent with what you want to change now?

Think of your toxic witches. What have they cost you in terms of people, finances, health, happiness, self-empowerment and overall well-being?

_____

_____

_____

_____

_____

_____

_____

How have your toxic witches impacted those you love around you?

_____

_____

_____

_____

If you do not change your toxic witches now, what will your life be like five years from now? Who will no longer be in your life? What will your finances, health, and happiness look like?

_____

_____

_____

_____

_____

_____

What will your life be like ten years from now look like? What will if look like twenty years from now?

_____

_____

_____

_____

_____

_____

_____

Think a bit ahead. What is your life like now that you have successfully made those changes and detoxed from these witches? How is this impacting those around you? Your work? Your health?

_____

_____

_____

_____

Imagine yourself five years from now because you have made these changes? What do you now see, hear or feel about your life? Who is in your life? What is your work like? Your health?

_____

_____

_____

_____

_____

Now, jump ten years ahead and imagine that you are walking through your home. You walk past the living room and hallway, past the kitchen area and into your bedroom where there is a full length mirror. Walk over to the mirror and look at yourself ten years from now. Because you took the steps needed to detox from those witches now, *what do you see as you look into your own eyes? What do you say to yourself as you look into the mirror and into your eyes ten years from now? How does this feel?*

_____

_____

_____

_____

_____

_____

_____

CHANGE HAPPENS IN A NANO-SECOND!

The wonderful news is that once you choose to make the change(s) needed to detox from the witch or witches, your change(s) will happen quickly…in a heartbeat…… in a nano-second.

SELF–HYNOSIS – BODY, MIND, UNWIND

Doing self-hypnosis is one of the easiest and most natural processes we can do and perhaps the hardest things about self-hypnosis is just remembering to *do* it! You can do your self-hypnosis to talk to your subconscious anytime you have a few minutes to relax in a safe environment where you won't be disturbed. While the door to the subconscious is always open to us, there are *specific* times of the day when the door opens up just a bit more. This happens just before we doze off to sleep and as soon as we open our eyes from a good night's sleep. For this reason, I suggest that my clients do their self-hypnosis at least twice a day—just before they fall asleep and as soon as they awake. First be sure to write down one or two key suggestions that you want on an index card. Remember to word these in the positive (what you want, not what you do not want), in the present tense (as if already so), and have fun with the wording. Make it as fun and positively charged as possible. The subconscious *loves* this! Here are a few examples:

- I crave healthy foods in healthy amounts and love the way these foods taste in my mouth and keep me full all day!

- I am a workout goddess and have a thirst for working out each morning as soon as my feet jump out of bed!

- Each day my clothes are fitting me better and better and I look amazing as I love hearing all of the compliments from people around me.

- I am easily dropping the excess fat from my beautiful body at a rate that is healthy and delightful to me.

- How surprised am I each day as I get up and notice my knee is free of the discomfort! Whahoo!

- I am amazed at how much I love driving safely each day and how much I enjoy my freedom.

- I speak with ease and joy as I embrace sharing in front of others and the fact that other people want me to succeed brings a smile on my face and adds to my delight!

- I love being a public speaking junkie!

- Writing comes easy and effortlessly to me and the more I write, the more I feel fantastic!

- I see myself sitting down taking the test and correctly answering all questions in a timely manner, finishing it with ease and delight!

- How exciting it is that I fall asleep easily and have the most fantastic restful night and then wake up each morning well rested and energized!

- I am so excited about how easily I have become a non-smoker and how this has no ill effects upon my body. It feels fantastic to be a non-smoker and I am a non-smoker for the rest of my long happy and healthy life!

Are you getting the idea here? Now take a few minutes to carefully construct your own super charged suggestions: Positive; In the Present Tense; Exciting! Remember that you cannot change someone else or a potential toxic situation, you can only change the meaning you give to that other person, emotion, and situation.

_____

_____

_____

_____

_____

_____

Now pick your favorite number from 1-9 and write this down on an index card.

Step 1. Once you have your 2-3 suggestions, read them to be sure that they really excite you and that they are doable and that they express what you really want. Then write them down on an index card. Write down your favorite number from 1-9 on the card.

Step 2. As you get into bed, read the suggestions 4-5 times, then put the card away and say that you are turning off the light switch I like to actually do the motion with my finger of turning down the switch.

Step 3. Shift your thoughts away from the suggestions on the card. Only think of your special number. In my case, it is the number eight. Think only about your number as you touch your thumb and finger together to make a little circle or zero.

Step 4. Just say to yourself that you are going to do your self-hypnosis for one to two minutes and then you will either go off to sleep (if it is your time to sleep), or you will awaken feeling refreshed and rejuvenated ready to take on the world!....or at least your new suggestions.

Step 5. Take 2-3 nice deep breaths in through your nose and out through your mouth as you touch your fingers together making a little circle as you think about your special number. Imagine seeing your number in three dimensions, paint the number pink with purple polka dots, twirl your number around, and turn it upside down. Think only of your special number as you take nice deep breaths and touch your thumb and finger together. Don't force this. If it comes it comes, if not just be patient. Your subconscious already now knows what you want and it will make it so. Just allow yourself to go into a restful sleep for the night.

In order to get the best results, repeat this as soon as you open your eyes in the morning before getting out of bed. Feel free to practice your self-hypnosis throughout the day. Do your self-hypnosis at least twice a day for thirty days. Most of my clients tell me they start to see major results within two weeks. Everyone is different. How committed are you to having your change(s)? Be sure to thank yourself and celebrate for all of the wonderful things that are already coming your way! How are you going to celebrate!

USING ALL OF OUR SENSES–HYPNOSIS, TAPPING, FOOD, AROMATHERAPY

Our subconscious, the center of all powerful and lasting change, is very *sensual* indeed. It *loves* the use of all of our senses- touch, hearing, and feeling, tasting, and smelling. As a matter of fact, the fastest way to get through the *critical factor* (gatekeeper) is to directly engage any of our senses. Think if how your mind feels when you are receiving a gentle and comfortable massage. If done correctly, your conscious mind seems to float away and has been sent off to *Cleveland* and is nowhere to be found. The same can be said of any time we are fully engaged in reading a good book or eating an amazing meal. We are in the present moment and are in the best state of all to take on any toxic thoughts, people, situations that may come our way.

While everyone utilizes all of their senses, our mind tends to favor one or two in particular. This varies person to person and no one sense is better or more important than the other. Some people are especially visual and love to see images. They use words such as "I *see* your point" and "Can you *picture* what I am saying". Others are more auditory and tend to experience the word through their sense of hearing. They use words like, "I *hear* you", and "You are not *listening* to me". Other people are kinesthetic and feel both physically and mentally. They may say, "I *feel* really happy" or "You *touch* my heart". In general we have a predominant sense and a secondary one. A smaller group of people tend to favor the sense of taste (gustatory), "That comment leaves a funny *taste* in my mouth" or our sense of smell (olfactory), "I can sense a *whiff* of success coming my way".

Hypnosis can elicit the power of any of our senses and is especially effective when matched to the primary sense of the person being hypnotized. A trained hypnotist will take the time to help determine which is the primary sense used by their client and adapt suggestions and hypnotic inductions to match their primary sense. Take a moment and write down words that you commonly use. Write down a description of what it was like when you first learned how to drive. Use as many descriptive adjective as possible to describe this experience. Are you visual, auditory, kinesthetic, gustatory, or olfactory based?

_____

_____

_____

_____

_____

_____

My Primary Descriptive Sense is: _____

Now go back and take the 2-3 suggestions you came up with for yourself and add wording in alliance with your special sense(s). Feel free to combine several senses if they seem right for you and you like the result. For example, "I love the way healthy foods feel in my mouth and keep me full all day long. I love the vibrant colors of healthy fruits and veggies, especially the bright reds, greens, and oranges". Your turn:

_____

_____

_____

_____

_____

Understand that E.F.T. (Tapping) uses many of our senses too- the sense of touch, hearing and sight. Pretty interesting stuff, yes?

AROMATHERAPY

Perhaps one of the most fascinating facts of all is that the one sense that goes directly to our brain, bypassing everything, is our sense of smell. Attached to our nose is a set of nerves from the olfactory bulb that goes right to our brain. It is like having a giant nerve hanging from our brain to our nose. This serves a major purpose. If we were to smell food that is rancid and poisonous, our nose will immediately pick this up before the food goes into our mouth and we immediately stop the food from entering our body. We also know the smell of fresh foods that will cause us to salivate and crave eating.

Our sense of smell is perhaps 20,000 times stronger than any other sense. Just one micro drop of a scent molecule (way too small for us to recognize consciously) will instantaneously elicit vivid memories and reactions—both physically and mentally. It is our sense of smell that gives us the majority of pleasure when we eat food. Taste is strongly connected to smell. Those people who suffer from *anosmia* (the loss of the ability to smell), often drop unhealthy amounts of weight as they consequently lose their appetite for food.

The use of scent can bring back wonderful vivid experiences that may have eluded us for a long time, such as the smell of apple pie and pumpkin spices that teleport us back to our grandmother's kitchen long ago and with happy memories as a young child. The beauty of Aromatherapy, which is the use of essential oils for health and well-being, is that it can be a very easy, portable, and immediate means of bringing about detox and change. We have all experienced this. If we are tired, a whiff of true essential oil of peppermint can uplift our spirits. If we are a bit anxious and on edge and in need of a change, a breath of pure essential oil of lavender will help us let go and be more relaxed. So in essence, pun intended, we can use key essential oils to help us get into a strong resourceful state of mind to help purge out toxic thoughts, people and places.

Synthetics scents do not work well and may cause allergic reactions. Oils that are *cut* with carrier oils, that is to say they are diluted with vegetable oils, are not as effective either. When using essential oils always use the best medicinal quality available. Allergic reactions are very rare when using pure essential oils as they are the life force of seeds, roots, flowers, fruit, bark from plants, trees, and shrubs and contain no allergy creating proteins. These oils are generally ones that you won't find at the supermarket or even the health food store. **I have a note in the resource section of this book to help you find therapeutic grade oils and blends as well as effective diffusors for home or office.**

High grade oils are not inexpensive, and yet the good news is that they are very concentrated and will last you a very, very long time. Here are a few oils and I use with my clients and I hope they can be of service to you. Always check with yourself or a client first before using any oil in case they do have a sensitivity or negative connection to the oil. For example, I adore the scent of precious rose, yet some people associate the memory of a funeral or death with rose. Everyone is unique so have fun experimenting and be respectful of the reactions and wishes of others:

Lavender: Relaxing, calming, aids in sleep

Rosemary: Uplifting and helps to bring about focus and concentration.

(I like to use a blend of equal parts Lavender and Rosemary in my office diffusor to help clients become focused and relaxed at the same time. This is a great blend for study and test taking and to have on hand any time you are involved in public speaking.)

Lemon: Very uplifting and sunny. Just imagine how it looks, feels, tastes, and smells when you cut into a fresh juicy lemon. Yowzer!

Orange: I love to have the scent of orange surround me as I am working. Just one little whiff and I can just see the happiness around me. This is always a quick pick-me-up when I feel a bit blue.

Geranium: One of my favorites, especially when working with women. It is uplifting and helps to balance emotions.

Frankincense: Not everyone may like this scent and yet it can be very powerful and relaxing.

Again, no one nose is the same—trust your own and take a whiff to know what works best for you or what works for your clients.

At the end of this section I will give you several recipes on the use of essential oils to bring about balance and well-being. You can invest in a wonderful diffusor to run in your home or office. To make it really simple, just put a few drops of an essential oil or blend on a tissue and carry it around with you.

DEVELOPING AN ATTITUDE OF GRATITUDE

As you take back ownership of your own body and mind and begin to unwind into relaxation and power, one of the strongest ways to keep this momentum going is to become aware of what you are truly grateful for. What is it that has become truly important to you? Remember back to Chapter Four and finding what you truly want. What you want is never a verb, as in to *make a lot of money, or exercising every day.* These things are simply strategies that may get us to what we ultimate want- joy, peace, love, connection, significance, variety and excitement. For example having money is a *strategy.* How will this *strategy* help you get what you truly want? If a strategy does not connect to what you want, you may want to change the strategy.

NEXT STEPS

Go back to what you wrote in Chapter Four when you discovered what it is you truly want.

What I truly want is: _____

_____

Ask yourself: What have I learned today that has helped me achieve what I really want?

_____

_____

_____

What have I learned from this book that is leading me to having what I truly want?

_____

_____

_____

What strategy can I think of that will help me achieve what I truly want? What am I willing to do to get what I truly want?

_____

_____

_____

What am I not willing to do to get what I want?

_____

_____

_____

What/who do I have now in my life that I am truly grateful for:

_____

_____

_____

Always stay focused on what you want because where you look is where you will go. If you focus on the things that truly make you happy in life, you will have a very happy life indeed.

KEY TAKE AWAYS:

- Make the decision and choice that you no longer will accept or put up with any crap from the bad toxic witch.

- Make the decision to change and know specifically what this change looks, feels, and sounds like.

- Have fun practicing your self-hypnosis using suggestions that are positive and in the present tense, with fun exciting words that match your prominent sense

- Aromatherapy and therapeutic grade essential oils are like a pocket detox pair of ruby red slippers. You can use them just about any time to get you to where you want to go.

DETOX RECIPE #7
Relaxing or Invigorating Baths

Never underestimate the power of taking a nice tub bath. I know that whenever I feel *totally* depleted, I step into my bath and I am once again *Queen of the Universe!*

For a relaxing bath which is great at the end of the day:

Ingredients:

1. Your favorite high quality relaxing essential oils such as Lavender, Orange, Sandalwood, Rosewood, Cedarwood, Geranium, Patchouli, Frankincense and Ylang-Ylang (Note: for the source of high quality essential oils and diffusors, please see the resources section of this book). List your preferred oil(s) here: _____

_____

2. High quality organic sea salt

3. A glass bowl to mix in

4. A stainless steel or wooden spoon to blend the oils with

Directions:

Add 1-2 drops of the oil or make a little blend by adding 1 drop of Lavender with 1 drop of Ylang-Ylang or 1 drop of Sandalwood with 1 drop of Orange- add to two Tablespoons of sea salt and mix in the glass bowl. Cover with parchment paper and allow them to blend and dry a bit for a couple of hours. (Make the day/night before).

Add to your bath at your preferred temperature and get in for a soothing soak.

For an invigorating and uplifting bath to help welcome a new day:

The same as above using invigorating oils such as a drop of Peppermint, Rosemary, Basil, Ylang-Ylang (can be both relaxing and uplifting), Orange (both soothing and uplifting), and Bergamot. Don't use more than 2 drops total in your mix per bath as these are strong oils. The oils I choose are:

_____

_____

DETOX RECIPE #8

Secret Ninja trick to help prepare for a test, public speaking or other time when you want to perform at your best.

Here is my secret, I prepare a blend of oils such as 2-3 drops of Lavender and 2-3 drops of Rosemary on a tissue and as I study or prepare, I continuously smell my power blend. Soon my subconscious will *link* all that I have studied and prepared for with this scent. When I go to perform, I simply take my tissue with me. By doing this my mind will bring up all the preparation that I previously did. Furthermore, the blend is usually very calming and relaxing to help with any *toxic* fear response. Sound too good to be true? Try it. Be sure to use an oil or blend that is really pleasing to you and not to overpowering to others. Again, my favorite is equal parts Lavender with Rosemary.

Here are a few other blends to try:
(1 drop of each on a tissue or cotton ball)

Ylang-Ylang with Clary Sage

Orange with Lemongrass

Rosewood with Sandalwood

Lemongrass with Lavender

CHAPTER EIGHT

ADDITIONAL RESOURCES TO TAKE YOU OVER THE RAINBOW

A BRIEF HISTORY OF THE USES OF HYPNOSIS

Hypnotic or suggestive therapy has been used as a healing technique since the beginning of history. It was of prime importance in the "sleep temples" of Ancient Greece, which were important places of pilgrimage and renewal.

In the Middle Ages belief in miraculous cures associated with religious shrines was widespread. Healing was brought about by touch and prayer.

During the 18th century the theory of "Magnetism" was developed. Franz Anton Mesmer argued that the planets influenced mankind through their magnetic effects on the "fluid" which occupied all space. He discovered that he could induce people into a trance-like state and concluded that he himself must be a kind of magnet, hence the term "Animal Magnetism". This idea was soon discredited by a French Royal

Commission, which found that the magnetic fluids did not exist. James Braid re-examined Mesmerism in the 19th century and reached similar conclusions. It was he who coined the term "hypnosis" for the induction of a trance-like state through simple suggestion.

In the early part of the 20th century hypnosis was used almost exclusively by stage hypnotists, thereby projecting a hopelessly distorted view of the very powerful therapeutic tool. However, in 1955 the British Medical Association endorsed the practice of hypnosis in medical school education, and in 1958 it was recognized by the American Medical Association as a healing modality. Since then hypnotism has become a valuable addition to conventional medical treatment.
Provided by www.WorldHypnotismDay.com © 2006

DEFINING NEURO-LINGUISTIC PROGRAMMING

Dr. Richard Bandler invented the term "Neuro-Linguistic Programming" in the 1970s. He was recently asked to write the definition of Neuro-Linguistic Programming that appears in the Oxford English Dictionary. It says:

Neuro-Linguistic Programming: "a model of interpersonal communication chiefly concerned with the relationship between successful patterns of behavior and the subjective experiences (esp. patterns of thought) underlying them" and "a system of alternative therapy based on this which seeks to educate people in self-awareness and effective communication, and to change their patterns of mental and emotional behavior."

According to *NLP Life* (http://www.nlplifetraining.com/what-is-nlp/index.html) the process of N.L.P. Is a method of influencing brain behavior (the "neuro" part of the phrase) through the use of language (the "linguistic" part) and other types of communication to enable a person to "recode" the way the brain responds to stimuli (that's the "programming") and manifest new and better behaviors. Neuro-Linguistic Programming often incorporates hypnosis and self-hypnosis to help achieve the change (or "programming") that is wanted.

E.F.T. QUICK REFERENCE

What is E.F.T. and what is it good for?

E.F.T. helps to neutralize unresourceful emotions by gently tapping with two fingers on various stress relief points on the face, hands and upper body to restore the body's natural flow of positive energy.

E.F.T. can be helpful for many fears, excess anger, study habits, public speaking, sports improvement, weight and food craving concerns, physical discomfort (when medically approved), help breaking habits such as smoking.

E.F.T. helps clear blocked energy patterns that are stuck in our body. The key points that are tapped work key meridian points to help unblock and move the energy out.
"All Matter is Energy" – Albert Einstein
"Energy is All That Matters" – Lois Brown

E.F.T. utilizes common spots that we touch: Rub under our eyes; Massage temples; Face in hands; Scratching our heads

Where is your favorite spot to touch/rub?

E.F.T. also helps "overload" the brain's limbic system, a primitive area of emotions, memories, fears, cravings by activating the senses of touch, sight, sound to help "reset" this area like the "restart" button on a vacuum cleaner or computer.

Who Created E.F.T.?

E.F.T. was first created by the psychologist, Dr. Roger Callahan, in 1979 and has since been improved by Gary Craig, who coined the phrase Emotional Freedom Technique. You can find further information at www.emofree.com. Their belief is that excess negative emotions are influenced by a disruption in the body's natural energy system.

What is the Process?

1. **State the Issue:** What is your issue? What is bothering you? What are you feeling?

2. **What is the intensity of Your Issue on a Scale of 0-10?** "10" is the worst intensity, "0" is no intensity – If you don't know – take a guess.

3. **Specific Statement of the Issue or Set-up Phrase:** "Even though I have this FEAR OF PUBLIC SPEAKING, I completely accept and love myself" - Understand that it is nearly impossible to resolve any issue until you begin to accept it and yourself as well. - Karate Chop on the side of either hand with two fingers as you say the set-up phrase. Say the setup phrase out loud with enthusiasm 3 times while tapping the karate point.

4. **The Tapping Sequence:** Tap each of the 8 points 6- 7 times while saying the issue: example: "This fear of public speaking". (see Tapping Chart)

5. **Take a Deep Breath and Reassess Your Intensity Level from 0- 10:** Where are you now?

6. ****Repeat the Tapping Sequence (#4) With Adjusted Statements:** For example tap while saying "This remaining fear of public speaking". Keep repeating the process as your intensity reduces down to a level of 2 to 0. If higher than a 2, keep at it.

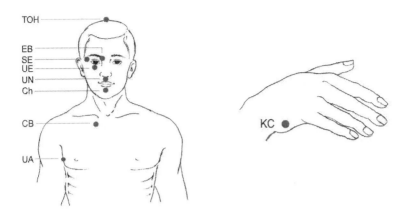

Please see www.emofree.com for this chart and further information about EFT from its founder, Gary Craig.

Karate Chop (KC) area of one hand; and the general tapping points: TOH= Top of Head; EB = Eye Brown; SE = Side of Eye; UE= Under Eye; UN = Under Nose; Ch = Chin; CB = Collar Bone; UA = Under Arm

HYPNOTIC DETOX RESOURCES

Lois Brown

www.HypnoticDetox.com

www.ThePrincetonCenterForHealth.com

www.HypnoticSoaps.com

a. Aromatherapy Essential Oils and Diffusors

b. Emotional Freedom Technique (E.F.T. or Tapping)

c. Hypnosis Programs and Sessions: In person and via Skype

d. Hypnotic Detox Soaps

e. Hypnotic Detox Teas

f. Hypnotic Detox recordings and MP3s

Books by Nurse Patricia Crilly

Tap It and Zap It!
Subtitle: A Grownup's Guide to EFT for Kids

Extraordinary Healing, Ordinary Miracle
Subtitle: Choosing Well-Being over Fearing Cancer

To Contact Christina Pirello
www.ChristinaCooks.com

CHAPTER NINE

CONCLUSION

"You've always had the power"

For far too long, far too many of us have given our power away to others. We have done this in the form of quick-fix pills and potions, advertisers telling us what we should look like, do and buy, and trendy diet books and false wizards. Always question what is being *thrown* your way and ask, "Are you a good witch or a bad witch?" In terms of toxic foods, habits, thoughts and situations, know that you must first make the key choice to *want* to change for the better and then have the courage to look behind the curtain to see the truth. The truth will indeed set you free.

The truth is, you have *always* had the power to take back ownership of your body and make the changes you want to get into that state of health and well-being that supports you to have a long and wonderful life. As Tony Robbins would say, "Everything you need is (already) within you *now.*" You are *always* the one driving your car. Perhaps you just needed someone to sit patiently besides you, calmly holding the G.P.S. That copilot can help you first figure out where it is you specifically want to go and to remind you to celebrate like crazy when you make all the correct turns to get you there. So get an accountability buddy– someone you respect and trust who will lovingly and firmly keep you on track. Perhaps this is someone you can support as well.

Stay connected with people who empower and appreciate you. Go where you are celebrated and not just tolerated. Be sure to ask yourself empowering questions every day. Never ask *why*—you most likely already know *why* and this will not solve anything. Ask *what* needs to happen to change? *What* needs to happen next? We have only just begun to realize the power of our minds, so experiment and write down what you are learning. You deserve the best! Have fun and celebrate each of the successes you are having along the way!

ABOUT THE AUTHOR
LOIS R. BROWN

Lois' commitment to her clients is based on the concern that people may be selling themselves short and settling for therapy that doesn't work and she wants them, instead, to have the life that they know deep down they can have.

Lois began her interest in this field at the age of 5, watching her father do self-hypnosis for his own health. She holds a Bachelors and a Masters degree in English Education from N.Y.U. Lois received her nutrition counseling training in New York City at the Institute for Integrative Nutrition and S.U.N.Y. at Purchase.

She studied with Tony Robbins and graduated from his Trainers Academy and has staffed at many of his events. In addition to hypnosis she utilizes Robbins Neural Associative Conditioning.

To maximize therapeutic impact, she is certified in Neural Linguistic Programing (N.L.P.) under its co-founder, Dr. Richard Bandler. She is also certified by Dr. Jaime Feldman, of the Institute of Hypnotherapy in the area of "Advanced Parts Therapy".

The Princeton Center for Hypnosis helps people achieve their goals by helping them take simple steps to improve their health; stop smoking, drop weight, overcome fears, overcome stress, improve study and test taking skills, and improve athletic performance.

Professional Member and with: The National Guild of Hypnotists; the International Hypnosis Federation; The American Association of Drugless Practitioners.

Lois lives near Princeton, N.J. with her husband-muse, Christopher Brown. They are both very proud of their amuse-muse son, David Brown.

You can reach Lois at:
    www.HypnoticDetox.com
    www.ThePrincetonCenterForHealth.com
    www.ThePrincetonCenterForHypnosis.com

REVIEWS

WHAT PEOPLE ARE SAYING ABOUT "HYPNOTIC DETOX: RECIPES FOR WELL-BEING"

"Lois takes toxic issues and serves up easy to digest bite-size solutions. Think of it as hor d'oeuvres for the mind, body and spirit."

Patricia Crilly, R. N.
Author of 'Tap it and Zap it' and the upcoming, 'Extraordinary Healing, Ordinary Miracle—Choosing Well-Being over Fearing Cancer'

"The techniques presented in this book are sound and easy to approach. Lois has completely removed any anxiety factor you might have with hypnosis by making you an active participant in the process. With the workbook-style pages peppered throughout, you remain fully in charge of what you want to achieve with hypnosis and wellness with Lois as your wise guide. Gentle, smart and fully present when you meet her, Lois brings those same qualities to this book to help guide humanity to well-being and balance."

Christina Pirello
Emmy Award winning host of PBS' 'Christina Cooks' and bestselling author of 7 cookbooks

"We are overwhelmed with information that becomes very challenging to sift through to find the truth among all the misleading and contradictions when it comes to our overall health. The key ingredient in order to follow any program to improve our health requires the powerful assistance of the mind. In her book Hypnotic Detox: Recipes for Well-Being Lois Brown puts it all together to create a clear and effective path to overall wellness and better living.

Tom Nicoli, BCH, CI, CPC
Personal Development Coach

Made in the USA
Middletown, DE
08 April 2015